S0-BCW-438

OUT-OF-SIGHT
OPTICAL
ILLUSIONS

J. Timothy Unruh
and
The Diagram Group

STERLING INNOVATION
An imprint of Sterling Publishing Co., Inc.

New York / London
www.sterlingpublishing.com

STERLING, the Sterling logo, STERLING INNOVATION, and the Sterling Innovation
logo are registered trademarks of Sterling Publishing Co., Inc.

10 9 8 7 6 5 4 3 2 1

Published by Sterling Publishing Co., Inc.
387 Park Avenue South, New York, NY 10016
© 2010 Sterling Publishing Co., Inc.

This book is comprised of materials from the following Sterling Publishing Co., Inc. titles:
Impossible Objects by J. Timothy Unruh © 2001
Visual Tricks by The Diagram Group © 2001

Distributed in Canada by Sterling Publishing
c/o Canadian Manda Group, 165 Dufferin Street
Toronto, Ontario, Canada M6K 3H6
Distributed in the United Kingdom by GMC Distribution Services
Castle Place, 166 High Street, Lewes, East Sussex, England BN7 1XU
Distributed in Australia by Capricorn Link (Australia) Pty. Ltd.
P.O. Box 704, Windsor, NSW 2756, Australia

Printed in China
All rights reserved

Sterling ISBN 978-1-4027-7160-6

For information about custom editions, special sales, premium
and corporate purchases, please contact Sterling Special Sales Department
at 800-805-5489 or specialsales@sterlingpublishing.com.

INTRODUCTION

Optical illusions of one kind or another have been of part of man's experience since the beginning of history. The mirage seen in the desert, the famous moon illusion—where the moon rising over the horizon looks so much larger than when seen high in the sky—the illusions created in light and shadow, and those of relative motion are just a few intriguing examples from the natural world. When these tricks of the eye and mind were first observed, they undoubtedly stirred the imagination. They were something that, upon closer examination, weren't as they appeared to be.

Through the ages optical illusions branched out and took on many forms. Some take the shape of two objects at the same time, others distort when viewed from different angles, some have objects hidden within larger pictures, and yet others confuse the eye by playing on how our minds interpret perspective.

In the graphic arts there is a fairly new strain of illusion that has become known as the "impossible object." Impossible objects involve manipulations of perspective and depth in two-dimensional drawings. Impossible in the real three-dimensional world, they function on misplaced perspective; depth inversions; misleading visual cues; discontinuity of planes; ambiguous coverings, shadings, and joinings; false and conflicting orientations and connections; altered vanishing points; and other "tricks" of the graphic artist.

This book contains optical illusions of every kind. You'll be challenged to spot differences between seemingly identical pictures, you'll learn the history and how to make impossible objects, you'll get dizzy staring down spirals that confound the eye and trick the mind.

Get ready for a visual feast!

The Impossible Triangle—The Tribar

This figure is probably the first formally published example of an impossible object. It appeared in the *British Journal of Psychology* in an article titled "Impossible Objects, a Special Type of Visual Illusion" in 1958. The authors, Lionel and Roger Penrose, father and son, a geneticist and mathematician respectively, referred to it as a "three-dimensional rectangular structure." It has also been called a "tribar" or a "warped tribar." Two other intriguing figures were also featured in the article. Thus, with these three, the "impossible object" was formally introduced into public awareness.

Soon afterward, the late and now very popular Dutch surrealist artist Maurits C. Escher (1898–1972) discovered the Penrose Triangle. At the time, he had just begun to be engrossed with the construction of impossible worlds. Subsequently, the Penrose Triangle, or the tribar, became the inspiration for Escher's extremely successful 1961 lithograph "Waterfall," which incorporated a clever linking of three tribars. In his drawing Escher essentially created a visually convincing perpetual-motion machine. It was perpetual in that it provided an endless watercourse along a circuit formed by the three linked triangles. Anyone who has been in a store where books and posters are sold has probably seen this image. Not only Escher but many others have copied and republished the tribar in their own varied forms, building upon the work that came before. The tribar is the first of the four great classic types of impossible objects, the others being the "Endless Staircase," the "Space Fork," and the "Crazy Crate."

When you first view the tribar, it looks like a simple drawing of an equilateral triangle. However, upon closer inspection, you see that there is something rather uncanny about it. The bars meeting at the top of the drawing appear to be perpendicular, while the bars at the lower left and lower right also appear to be perpendicular. Each corner presents a different angle to your eye. The triangle, or whatever you want to call it, is logically consistent in each of its individual areas, but is nonsensical overall. It is not truly warped, but only held together as a drawing through the incorrect connections of normal elements.

2 Melissa wants to add another block. Can she?

3 Can you read this message?

4 Triple Warped Tribar

The figure at the right is a simple but profound elaboration of the Penrose Triangle. That tribar exhibited a single impossibility, while this figure has many. As your eye examines this figure—as with any impossible object—you must reappraise the drawing at every turn. The object has a convincing solidity, but if you tried to build such a thing it just wouldn't work out. This is at the essence of impossible objects!

5 How many blocks are used in these shapes?

6 Which is closer to the line—the spider or the butterfly?

7 Twelve-Cube Triangle

Geometric shapes are the best sources of inspiration for developing impossible objects. Take the simple cube, for instance. We see thousands of them in one form or another every day. As you can easily see in the figure on the facing page, we took one of the tribars from a previous page and broke it down into cubes. By doing that nothing was lost: this figure is just as profoundly impossible as its predecessor!

Constructed of a dozen cubes, this arrangement was laid out on a draftsman's board with a plastic 30°/60° triangle. The drafting triangle was useful in making sure that the individual cubes conformed to the overall perspective of the drawing. The impossibility, which takes advantage of this perspective, is accomplished by the false foreground-background placement of the rows of cubes, an effect similar to the one in the tribar. In other words, the drawing is held together through the incorrect connections of the normal rows of cubes.

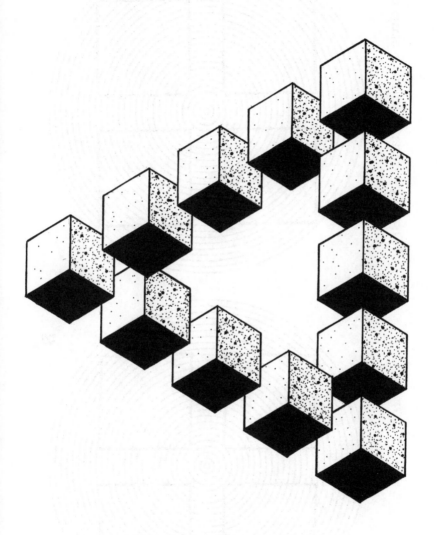

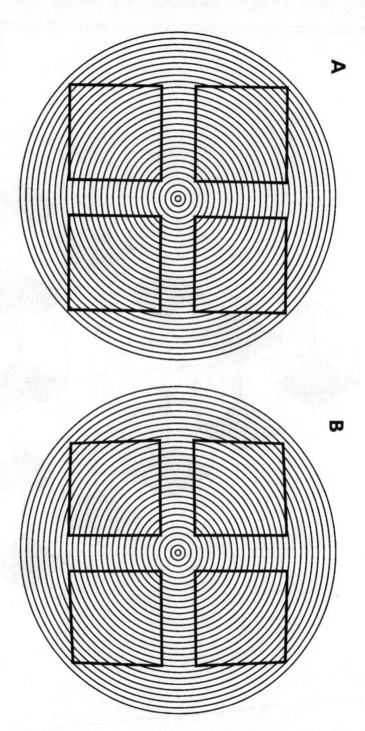

8 Which circle contains squares—A or B?

14

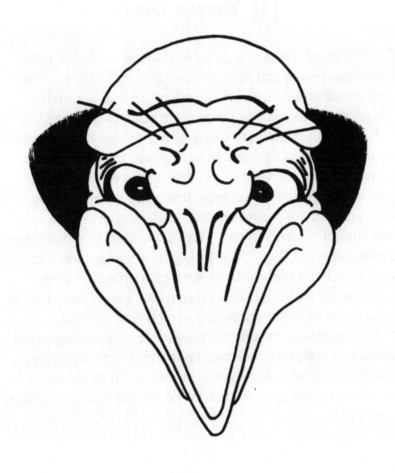

9 Can you find my brother? He is very happy!

10 Winged Tribar

The "Winged Tribar" is another elaboration of the tribar concept, which just goes to show how easy it is to create unique and intriguing new variations on a single theme. The tribar lends itself to many interesting variations!

For years psychologists have employed geometric figures of various sorts in their studies of human personality and behavior. Since the turn of the century more than 200 figures and illusions have been devised in order to analyze the psychology of seeing and the process of eye-brain dynamics of patients as they view these objects and attempt to make sense of them. Many insights about personality types have been derived from such experiments where incompatible information is given to the eye. A few of these figures even include impossible objects like this one.

It's interesting to watch someone viewing an impossible figure, and certainly entertaining to observe them trying to make sense of it. Impossible objects seem to be useful tools for psychologists in their quest to find out what makes people tick.

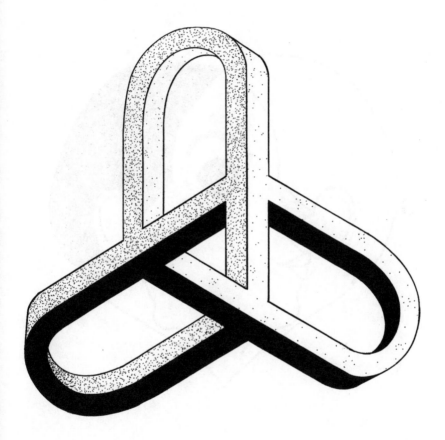

▐▐ Is she a blonde or a brunette?

12 How could these construction workers have built this building?

13 Tri-Domino

To accomplish what this three-piece suite appears to demonstrate would normally require four elements, not just three. Try it yourself the next time you play dominoes! To make a normal circle you need 360 degrees, but this object seems to close the 360-degree loop in just 270 degrees! Upon closer examination, it becomes apparent that this figure operates on a misplaced return in perspective—similar to that of the impossible tribar. This figure is really merely an impossible tribar in which the three perimeter elements have been replaced by the familiar game pieces.

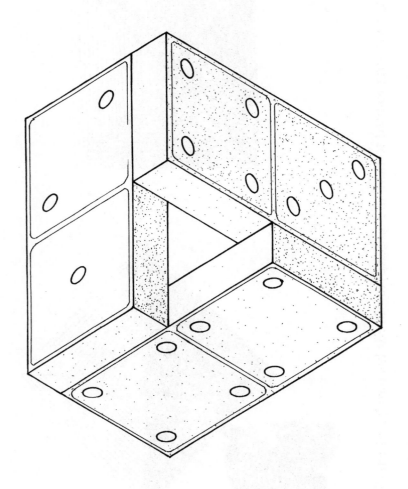

14 The Egyptian king wanted to have the larger pyramid for his family. Which did he choose?

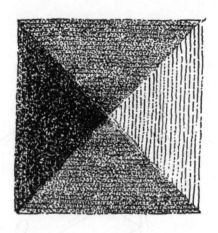

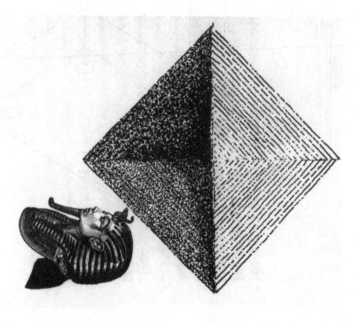

15 What's weird about this building?

16 Dowel Block

The more sophisticated version of the tribar principle, shown on the facing page, was inspired by a child's building block and a Tinkertoy™. This object consists of a pair of complementary dowel-like components that penetrate the block and then intersect outside the block at an impossible juncture. It is the juncture alone that makes this impossible object possible, at least on paper! That this profound figure is a triangle is evident even in this simple two-element composition.

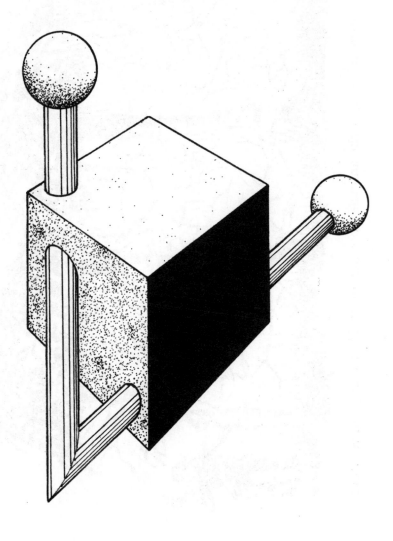

25

17 The huntsman is calling the animals from the forest. How many can you find?

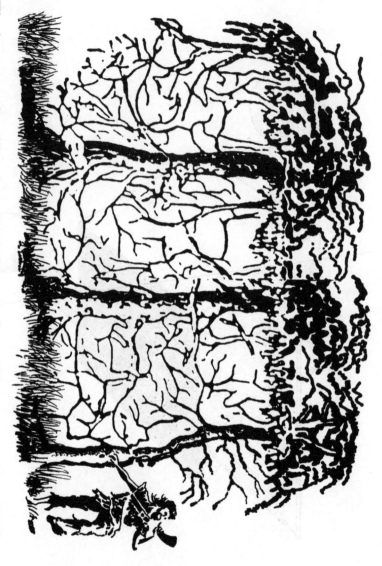

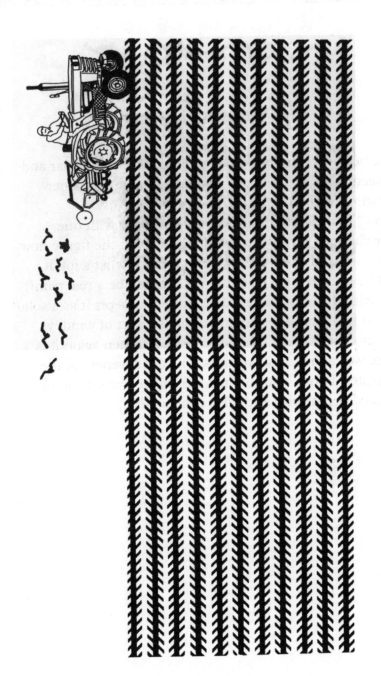

18 Jason entered a plowing competition to cut straight rows. Did he succeed?

19 Truncated Tribar

As we become more closely acquainted with the tribar and its seemingly limitless expressions, we now find a new and curious variation.

The "Truncated Tribar" is simply a tribar with one corner chopped off—"truncated." As a result the figure now has four sides. If this object were a window, what a job it would be to install the glass pane! (It would be a real pain!)

As with the impossible tribar, our eye accepts it as a solid object at first glance, but then sees it as a sort of window frame. It cannot really exist, of course, but then again it is a figure we cannot easily dismiss. The effectiveness of the "Truncated Tribar" illusion arises from a combination of misplaced perspective and false connections.

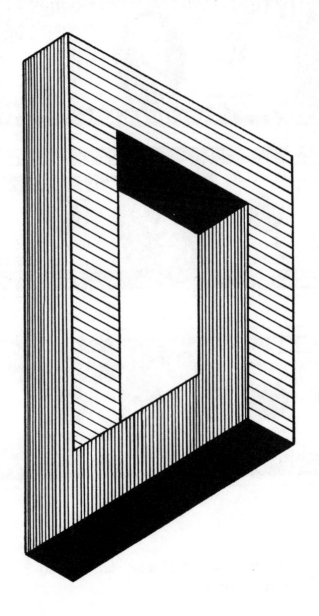

20 Are there any fakes? And if so, can you find the forger's mistakes?

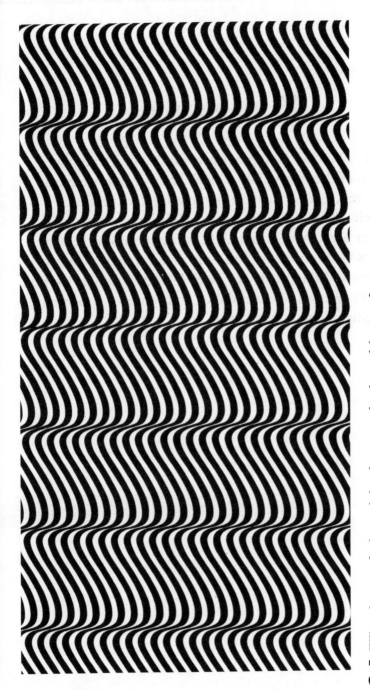

21 Why do you feel seasick when you look at this page?

22 Mental Blocks

Children's blocks? Computer graphics? No, it's another version of the impossible tribar! The cube, as we have already seen, is a very useful element in constructing impossible objects. This is a simple but intriguing triangular arrangement of cubes. It functions on the same dynamics as its ancestor. The only real differences between this figure and the previous "Twelve-Cube Triangle" is that this figure consists of fewer cubes and provides a mentally challenging and subtle variation.

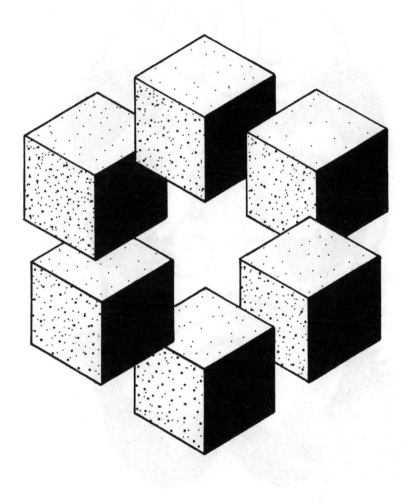

23 Melissa is drawing her dad, but Charles is drawing his uncle. Are they drawing the same person?

24 Does your brain say the image has gray lines across it side to side and top to bottom?

25 Diamond Crossover

The enigmatic figure on the facing page was derived from staring at a cross-truss that supported a stair landing at a two-level apartment complex. Again, the principle of the tribar is quite evident. The "Diamond Crossover" is essentially nothing more than two tribars glued together in the shape of a diamond. You could expand on this design by gluing together additional tribars here. As mentioned earlier, Escher attached three tribars in his famous composition. There really is no limit. In fact, you could glue many such tribars together in a pattern that would be very effective in a pieced quilt or some other design. Otherwise, we leave it to you, the observer, to triangulate this squeamish, squashed, squarish thing!

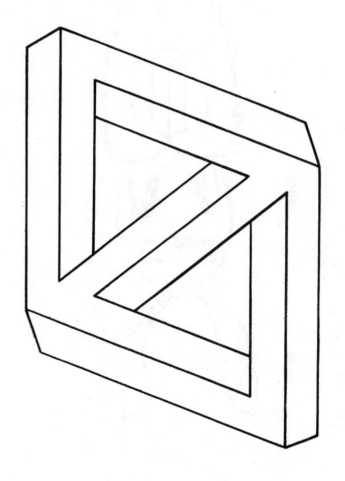

26 Mr. Egghead is looking for Mr. Rabbit. Can you help find the rabbit?

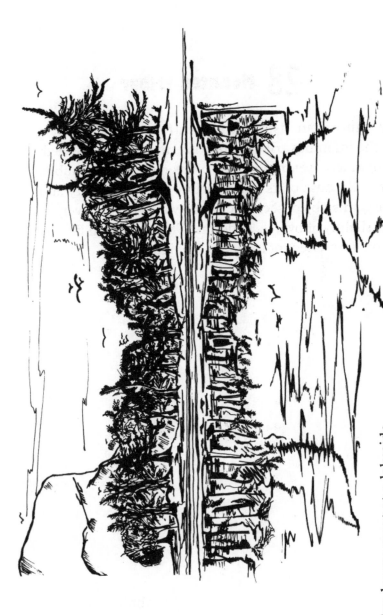

27 Two lovers meet at a lakeside. Can you find them?

28 Mounted Tribar

This figure is an instant replay, with more variations, of the infamous tribar. This time the object is placed appropriately (yet impossibly) on its own rack for public display. Because of its odd interface between reality and fantasy, this object seems to peel away and float over, or hover slightly above, its pedestal! The additional floating illusion is an effect of its depth ambiguity.

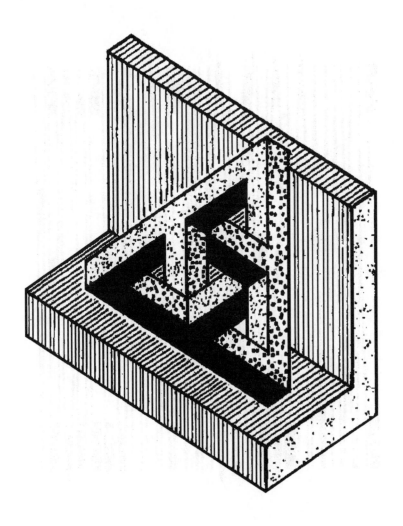

29 What does this say?

30 How many letters can you find in this pattern?

3 | Warped Tribar Truncate

The "Warped Tribar Truncate" is, in essence, another chopped-off, or truncated, tribar with some internal variation. It looks as if it could be a surrealist design for a new style of furniture, but would certainly stop cold any carpenter who accepted an order for a dozen of these things. Then again, this piece of very expressive mini-art could open up a host of new ideas for everything from lawn chairs to plaza sculptures!

The visual arts cater to a wide variety of human needs. Impossible objects, like this one, present an amusing interplay of intrigue and entertainment. They could be called "recreational art"!

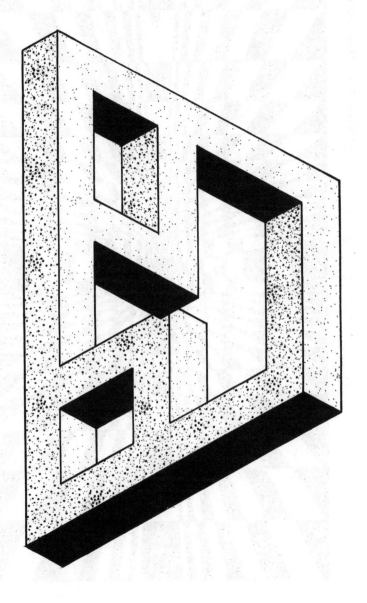

Which bomber is bigger?

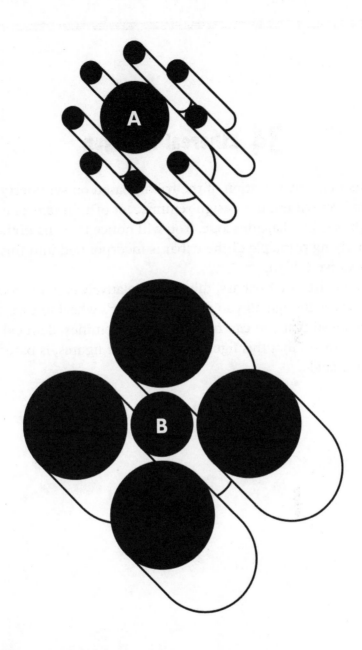

33 Peter had to select either A or B as the larger bucket. Which bucket would you choose?

34 Ethereal Hexagon

This rich new variation of the tribar, based on symmetry and repetition, is a design reminiscent of an image one might see in a kaleidoscope. You will notice that the grand underlying principle of the tribar is incorporated into this innovative design.

Like the other tribars, this one is relatively easy to create. It looks as though all you need is a potter's wheel to turn the drawing so that you can make all the extremities identical. It is easy to see that this figure, like all tribar figures, is based on a triangle.

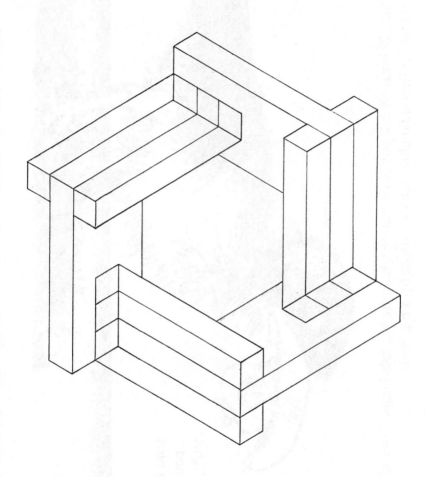

35 Beard-face Bob nearly fell out of his canoe when the big fish jumped out of the water. Can you find his granddaughter Chloe caught by a big bird?

His granddaughter Chloe screamed when the big bird got her.

36 There are six differences between the sets of State seals on this page. How many can you find?

51

37 Rectangular Trihedron

In this concluding example of the tribar theme, we see yet another intriguing way to elaborate on the Penrose Triangle. In case you're wondering if the tribar model is now exhausted, rest assured that new ideas will always be coming up—that's guaranteed!

In principle, this figure functions very much like the other members of the tribar family. It is basically a three-dimensional equilateral triangle made up of rectangular solids that cause your gaze to dance about from one extremity to the other in an attempt to make sense out of the figure.

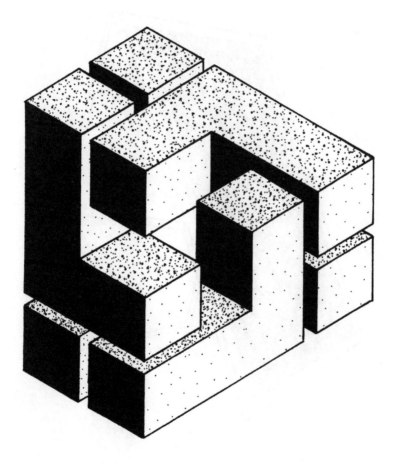

38 This sign outside the store has a mistake. Can you spot it?

39 How can the space traveler turn into a bandit?

40 The Endless Staircase

One of the best known of the great classics of Impossibilia, this figure is known most often as the "Endless Staircase." It has also been called the "Everlasting" or "Infinite Staircase" or the "Penrose Staircase," after its originators. It has also been referred to as "a continually ascending or descending path."

This figure was first published in 1958 by Lionel and Roger Penrose along with the tribar and another illusion in the *British Journal of Psychology*. In this illusion you are confronted with a stairway said to lead upward or downward without getting any higher or lower. On completion of one visual circuit, you find yourself back where you started. If you were to actually walk this stairway, you would find yourself uselessly ascending or descending into infinity and getting a great deal of exercise. You might call it the ultimate treadmill! Since the Penroses first published it, this impossible object has probably appeared in print more often than any other impossible object. You'll find it in books on games, puzzles, illusions, psychology, and other subjects as well.

The "Endless Staircase" was another figure put to great use by Maurits C. Escher, this time in his fascinating 1960 lithograph "Ascending and Descending." In his graphic, which explored the Penrose artifact to its fullest potential, the very recognizable "Endless Staircase" is neatly set into the rooftop of a monastery, on which a number of hooded monks of an unknown sect march perpetually clockwise and counterclockwise, passing each other as they continue in opposite directions around their impossible rooftop conveyance, never really managing to go up or down.

Consequently, the staircase has become more associated with Escher, who copied it, than the Penroses, who originated it.

A few years ago researchers at the Bell Telephone Laboratory produced a film featuring the "Endless Staircase." It shows a ball bounding endlessly in a circuit on top of the staircase. To enhance the effectiveness of this illusion a musical note sounds at each bounce and rises in pitch with each step up, but beyond the scale of a single octave the notes never seem to get any higher. After a number of steps up there is a pause, and then the next tone drops an octave but the brain fails to realize it. The ball and the music added to the "Endless Staircase" result in a most convincing and eerie, doubly impossible audiovisual illusion.

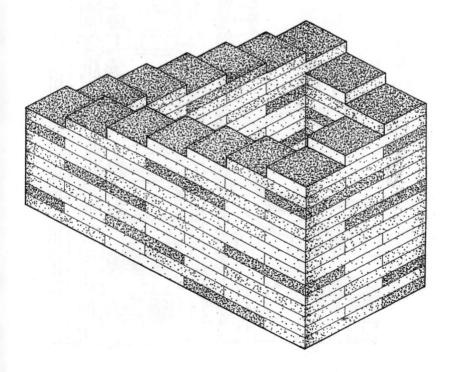

4 How can you reduce the number of lower arches to only four?

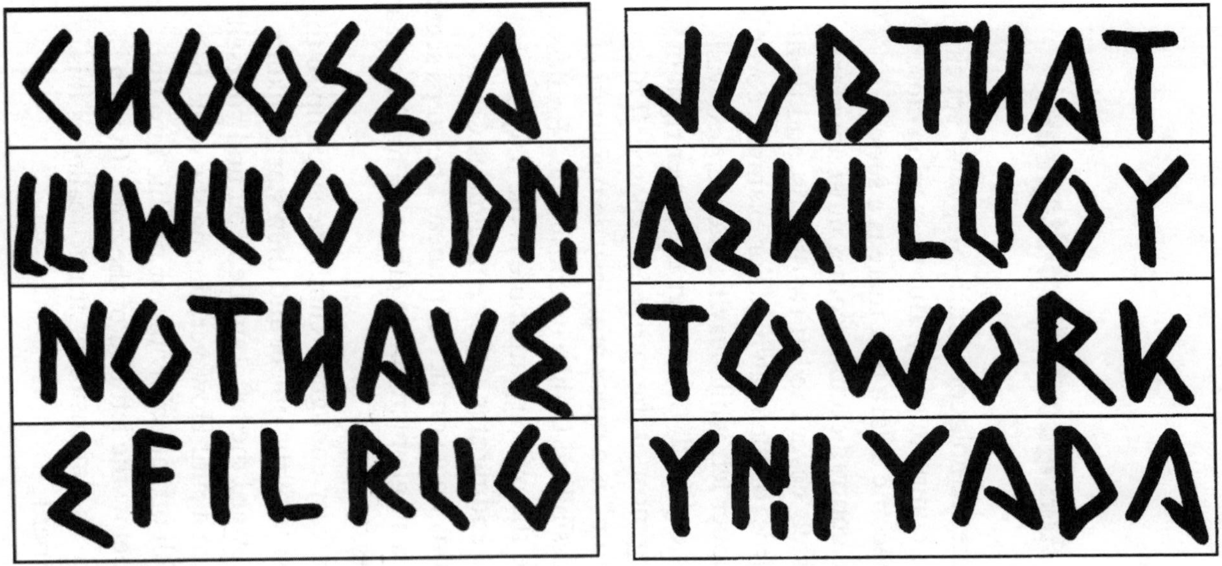

JOBTHAT

ASKILUOY

TOWORK

YNIYADD

CNUOSSΖΔ

IIIIUOYΛΠ

NOTWAVƎ

ƎFILRUO

42 The ancient Greeks wrote their words in opposite directions on each line. Can you read this example?

43 Ambiguous Curb-Stepway

At first glance the "Ambiguous Curb-Stepway" appears as a whole and complete entity. But then upon closer inspection you become aware that there is a serious incongruity. The contradiction becomes most apparent when you alternately cover the left two-thirds, and then the right two-thirds, of the drawing. For example, cover the curb at the upper left while leaving the stepped wall at the lower right exposed, then cover the lower right of the figure, leaving most of the curb end exposed. This "silent interrogation" is a quick and easy demonstration of the object's impossibility! Unlike its cousin the "Endless Staircase," where the primary attribute is the perpetual ascending or descending steps, the "Ambiguous Curb-Stepway" functions on a conflict of planes. The steps seem to emerge out of a single plane in an effect we might call a dual discontinuity.

It would seem easy enough to climb the steps up to the top on the right side of the object and then start walking along the plane toward the left, but then you find yourself back at the bottom again! However, during the walk, be careful lest you fall off into oblivion, or tumble into the stream of space below the left end of the curb. In such an ambiguous "cross-dimensional" fringe reality as this, anything can happen!

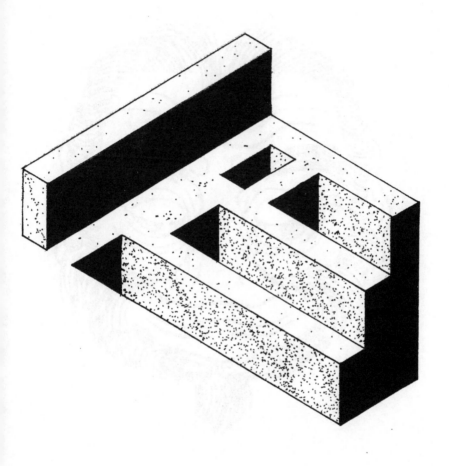

44 How does this leprechaun turn into a sumo wrestler?

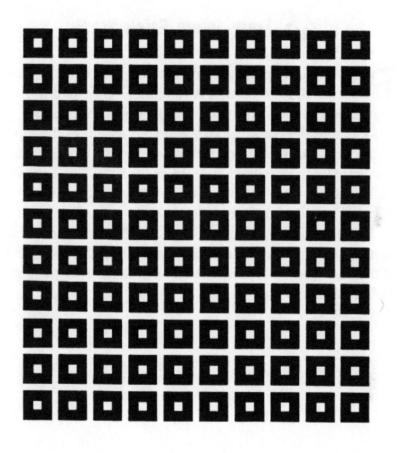

45 Are there really gray patches at the corners of the squares?

46 Four-Seven Stick Stack

This profusely stepped specimen could have been inspired by a stack of railroad ties. As a climber anticipating your negotiation of the steps, you have the option of taking it in four steps or seven. It looks as if your ascent to the top would be easier in an approach from the left. However, until you actually try it, you cannot know for sure. The laws of energy conservation and expenditure may not apply in this uncanny world of the impossible!

The illusion has been accomplished by taking advantage of its equally spaced parallel lines in treating the end detail of the sticks, some of which seem to twist in order to comply with the illusion.

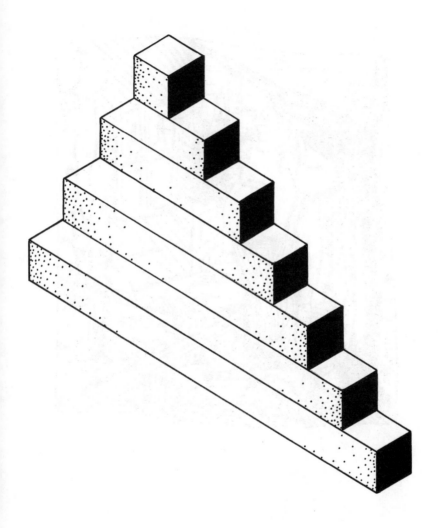

47 Potbelly Bill is trying to find his younger brother, Frank. Can you help him?

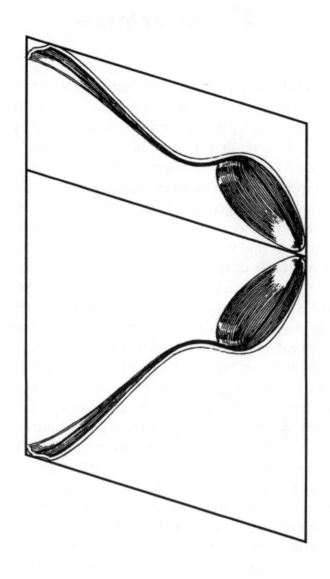

48 Which spoon is larger?

49 Zip-Step Vertigo

This figure, a cousin to the tribar as well as to the "Endless Staircase," could perhaps be the ultimate StairMaster—if you turned it on its side. You could place it in your living room or garage for use in your daily twenty-minute aerobic exercise—sideways or upright! This wonder unit of meta-science could provide any desired incline from zero to thirty degrees without requiring an adjustment. Since there are no moving parts (except yourself!), it would never wear out. The only prerequisite might be a high ceiling, and the only problems that you might experience would be uncanny recurrent attacks of vertigo and déjà vu!

Upon close inspection you'll see that the "Zip-Step Vertigo" is made up of two subtly interconnected tribars, one placed above the other. The continuity of the walkway seems unbroken—until you realize that you can't decide on the status of the ambiguous vertical shaft, which extends straight up from the front of the pathway, ending behind it at the top. Both the far and near extremities of the seemingly level pathway are thus impossibly connected by the same vertical shaft, when in reality there should be two shafts. Thus, if you start walking at the bottom and travel the zigzag path, you will reach the top of the shaft. If the shaft were a hollow chute, you would drop straight down, right back to where you started. It is this same effect that made Escher's "Waterfall" work so well. The "Crazy Crate," discussed later, exhibits a similar discontinuity, where you are faced with a strategic vertical element that exists both in the background and the foreground. You can avoid the conflict only if you are able to mentally block out the vertical element.

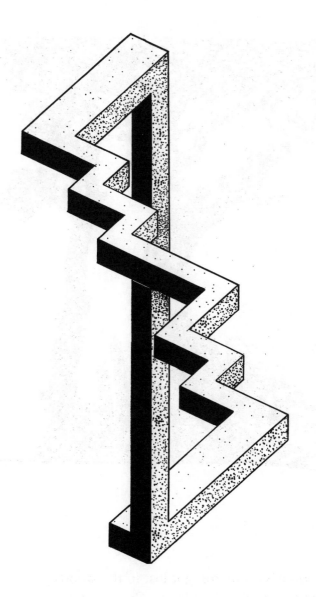

50 George Washington got lost in the woods while searching for his cat. Can you find them both?

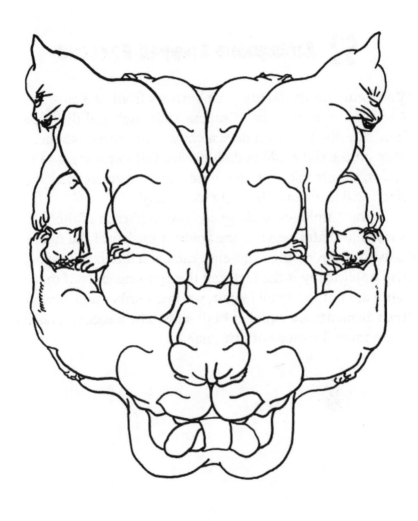

51 How many cats can you find in this picture?

52 Ambiguous Stepped Pyramid

The figure on the facing page borrows from two classic impossible forms, the "Endless Staircase" and the "Space Fork." In this case, you have a choice: you may take the route on the right side and climb five full steps to get to the top, or, simply take one step onto the platform at the left, which will lead you ethereally to the top!

In the "Ambiguous Stepped Pyramid" each of the horizontal shafts between the voids at the left of the figure leads to a step on the right end, each at a different level. Also noteworthy is the fact that the opposite ends of the figure are not the same length, yet the number and size of tread elements are equal at both ends. The nagging question is, are there five steps or just one?

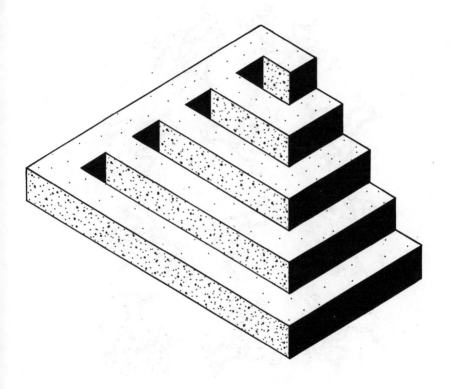

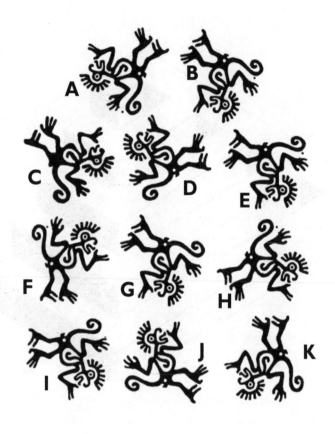

53 A professor in Mexico discovered a hoard of gold rings, each one bearing the image of a monkey. One, he decided immediately, was a forgery. Can you spot the fake?

54 Who uses this seal?

PRESIDENT OF THE UNITED STATES OF AMERICA

55 Incongruous Stepped Wall

This intriguing figure is another impossible object that adds to the complexity of this book. It combines subtle elements from both the "Endless Staircase" and the "Space Fork." These influences become evident, one way or another, when you examine the figure closely.

You will see that the figure is tied together by a single profound discontinuity: the front surface of the lower step "twists" toward the right and becomes a "floor" at the base of the wall. At the same time this effect causes us to confuse the opening in the wall with the shaded face of the second step.

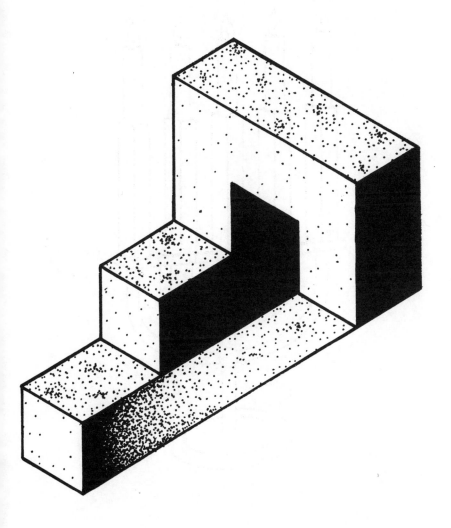

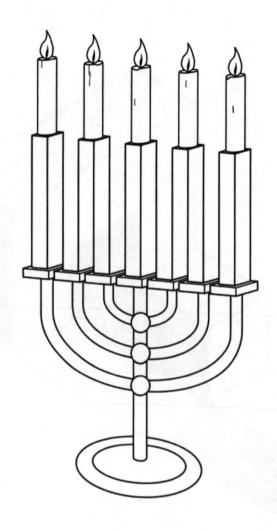

56 How can you have five candles filling a seven-candle holder?

57 Is this guy happy or unhappy?

58 The Space Fork

With the "Space Fork," we enter the very heart and essence of Impossibilia. It represents what is probably the largest distinct family of impossible objects. Almost everyone has seen it at one time or other. It was this object that appeared one day on Mr. Thomas's bulletin board in the author's high school woodshop class, labeled simply "Space Fork." Even though I was unsuccessful in building such an object, I still got an "A" in Thomas's class, not to mention the fact that his pin-up triggered my interest in impossible objects, which led to a lifelong pursuit.

The notorious three-(or is it two-?) pronged impossible object began circulating among engineers and others in 1964. It first appeared in print as part of an advertisement by California Technical Industries in the March 23, 1964 issue of *Aviation Week & Space Technology* magazine. An article was published later that year by a psychology professor at Iowa State University in Ames, Iowa. It appeared in the December 1964 issue of the *American Journal of Psychology*. This was the first published writing about this ambiguous figure, which the author, Dr. Donald H. Schuster, called a "three-stick clevis." An actual shift in visual fixation is involved in perceiving and resolving (if that were possible) the incongruity in this new type of ambiguous figure. After much attention, scrutiny, and creative variations made by others over the years, Schuster's "Space Fork" has become a classic. A visually ambiguous trident or clevis-like device, of absolutely no practical use, it has also been called by some, simply, a "blivet." One rep from an aerospace manufacturer has suggested that its attributes be investigated for the design of an interdimensional cosmic tuning fork!

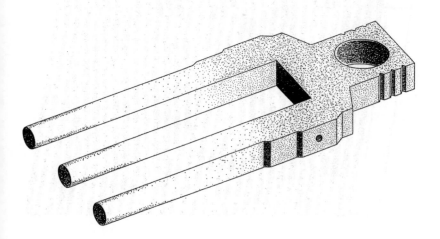

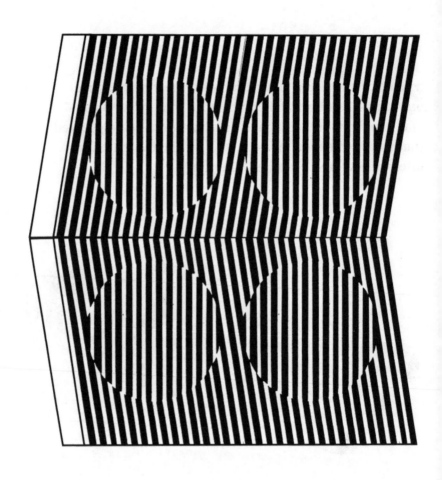

59 Do the lines on the disks slope down to the left or down to the right?

60 Do the sides of the arches join in the middle?

6 | The Space Fork

If you don't immediately perceive the impossibility of the object, it's probably due to the oscillation in your attention between the left and right sides of the figure. Each of them separately is possible as a two-dimensional representation of the same solid object, but not when viewed together from the same point in space.

The problem arises from an ambiguity in depth perception. Your eye is not given the essential information necessary to locate the parts, and your brain cannot make up its mind about what it's looking at. Your problem is to determine the status of the middle prong. If you look at the left of the figure, the three prongs all appear to be on the same plane; in other words, they seem to share the same spatial-depth relationship. Yet, when you gaze at the right of the figure, the middle prong appears to drop to a plane lower than that of the two outer prongs. So just exactly where is the middle prong located? It obviously cannot exist in both places at once. The confusion is a direct result of your attempt to interpret the drawing as a three-dimensional object.

The "Space Fork" works on the principle of the false connection—a connection that can be made on a two-dimensional plane or surface, but not in the three-dimensional world. The figure makes use of the fact that a prong, round in cross section, can be represented by a pair of parallel lines, while a beam, square in cross section, requires three lines. The illusion is constructed by completing each pair of lines to make a prong at one end, and each triad of lines to make a beam at the other end. The parallel lines are equally spaced to emphasize the contradiction. If you could make a cross-sectional "bread slice" cut through the middle of the "Space Fork," what do you think it would look like?

The figures shown below represent two variations on the "Space Fork."

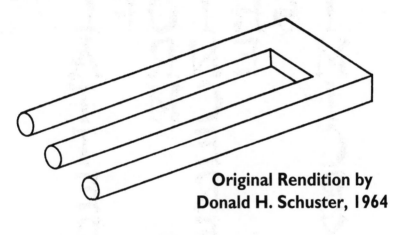

Original Rendition by Donald H. Schuster, 1964

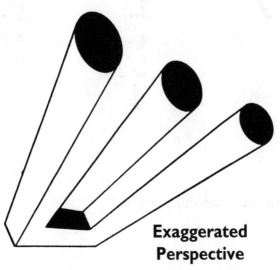

Exaggerated Perspective

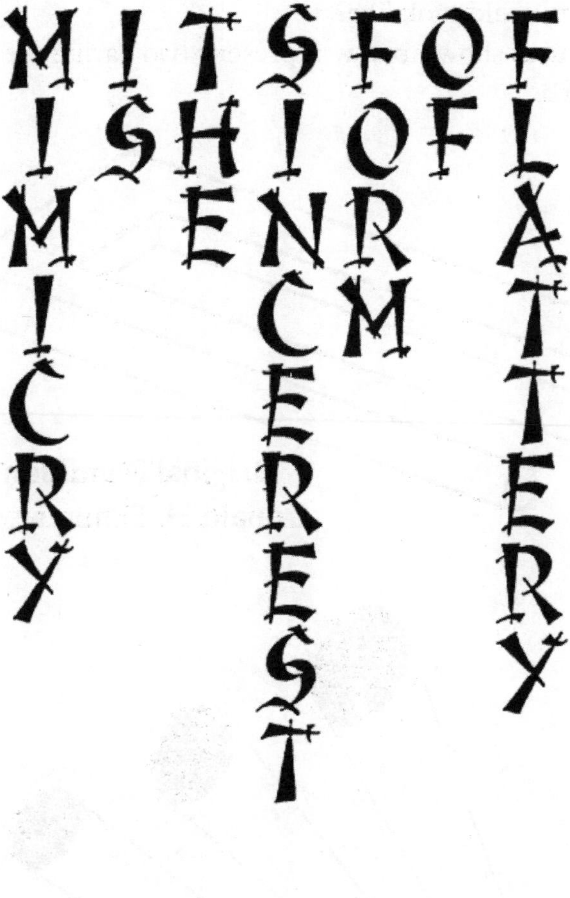

M I T S F O F
I S H I O F L
M H N R A
I E C M T
C N R T
R C E E
Y E R R
R Y
E
S
T

62 Can you read this message?

63 Can you identify these countries?

64 Ridge-Slotted Brick

The object on the facing page is a technical variation of the "Space Fork" illusion. As you can see, it clearly applies the principle of the "Space Fork," but while the "Space Fork" is free-floating, the "Ridge-Slotted Brick" is a floor-mounted fixture. In fact, if a metallurgist could be talked into fabricating such a thing out of iron, it might make a terrific interdimensional doorstop! The shop drawings could easily be drafted onto vellum, from which actual blueprints could be made. Of course, dimensioning the fluted top side might pose a problem, if the draftsman were to pay too close attention.

Like the famous "Space Fork," the "Ridge-Slotted Brick" functions on depth ambiguity. Convex edges at one end become concave at the other, while three distinct elements at one end dissolve into two at the other. The only real difference is that the three-two relationship is reversed, the trunk end being made up of three elements instead of two, as in the "Space Fork." Your problem, as you soon find out, is to establish order out of the continually chaotic, fluted top surface of the object. The confusion is a direct result of your attempt to interpret the drawing by conventional means. While the "Space Fork" uses precise parallel lines to expedite its illusion, the "Ridge-Slotted Brick" works best with lines that are slightly off parallel.

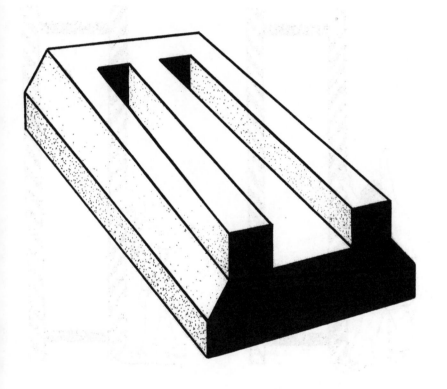

65 Bob insists that his poles are the same distance apart at the top and bottom. Lauren insists her poles are too. Who is right?

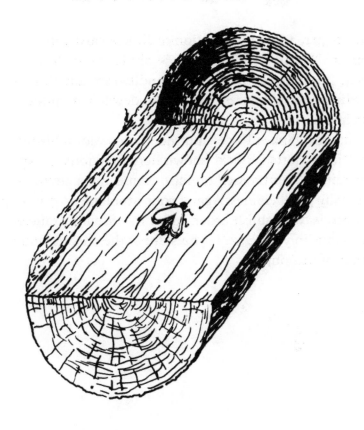

66 Is the fly on the top side of the log, or the bottom side?

67 Ridge-Slotted Block

This object, a third-generation technical variation on the "Space Fork" illusion, is similar to the last object. It is another in an almost endless stream of semi-interdimensional figures that can be developed on the principle of that classic.

Like the "Space Fork" and the "Ridge-Slotted Brick," the "Ridge-Slotted Block" shown here functions on an ambiguity in depth based on false connections between essentially parallel lines. Again, your problem, as you soon discover, is to establish order out of the visually induced oscillations in your gaze as you stare at the chaotic fluted surface of this object.

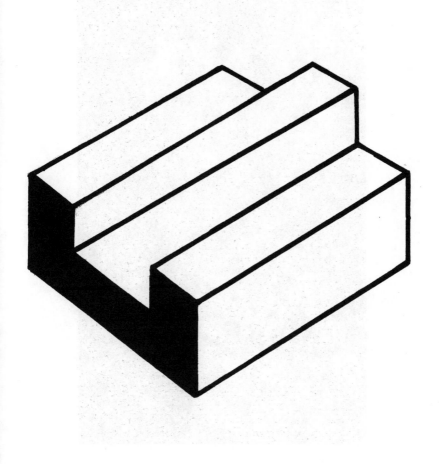

68 Can you tell what this is?

69 Paul's mom is calling him. Can you see where Paul is hiding?

70 Outland Toaster

Like the other innovations just described, this figure is very much akin to the "Space Fork," as a number of elements on one end mysteriously gain a member at the other. Only, in this case, the whole figure is turned upright.

If you were to think of this device as a simple toaster in which to brown your daily bread, your experience might be an intriguing one. Imagine, for example, taking two slices of bread and placing them in the "Outland Toaster." What might happen when they pop up? Will there be two pieces of toast, or three? Whatever the outcome, this device might be as sought-after as the long-awaited free-energy device, or the mythical perpetual-motion machine!

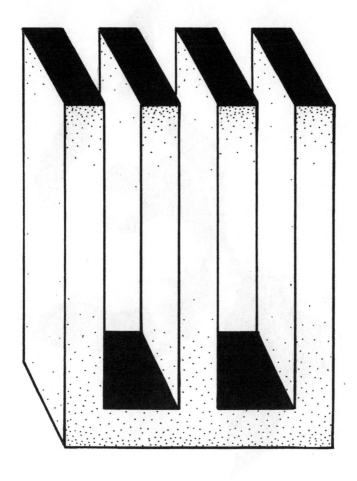

71 Do you know what part of the world these shapes belong to?

72 Is this a spiral? Try following one of the lines round to see.

73 Twin-Columned Quadra-Tower

The "Twin-Columned Quadra-Tower" exhibits, as its name implies, an obvious solid duality at its base. However, taking advantage of its parallel lines, the connections at the top produce an equally sound four-element crown piece. The visual ambiguity of this drawing overall is too great to resolve into a single solution. It is almost as difficult as imagining a square circle! This is another drawing where you can cover its lower two-thirds with your hand, and then move your hand down to amaze your friends with the big surprise at the bottom!

Like the "Outland Toaster," the curious object exhibited on the following page seems to hang on the "outland" of reality. Could it be a by-product of some bizarre government experiment? Or, could it be the schematic design for a midtown high-rise? At any rate, this odd structure seems to have the uncanny ability to materialize or dematerialize at will. Then again, maybe it could be used as a new type of storage dump for the disposition of hazardous materials and substances!

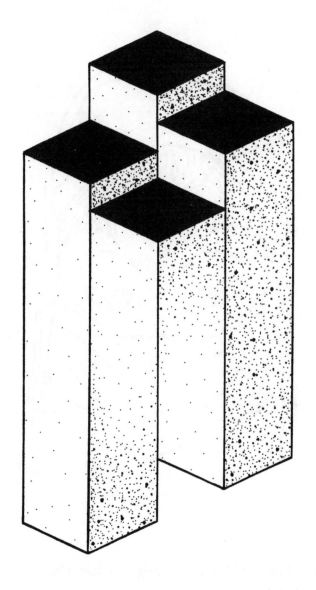

74 This Arab girl has a very angry father. Can you see him?

75 Which of the twelve dice is a fake?

76 Dual Tri-Quadra Structure

As with the illusion shown on page 101, the impossibility of the "Dual Tri-Quadra Structure" is accentuated by its strong vertical lines and texture. Here we see that the "magic" of impossible objects can be created not only from distortions in perspective or from contradictory visual cues, but from added horizontal or vertical textural peculiarities as well.

Another intriguing fact about this object is that is involves numeric indecision. Looking at the base, we see three pillars, from which we conclude that a total of four pillars supports the structure, assuming that one is located behind, hidden from view. Yet our assumption is not sound, for at the top we see that there are only three pillars, hence the name "Dual Tri-Quadra Structure"!

One interesting effect of impossible objects such as this is the sense of visual restlessness they seem to induce in the viewer. You will experience many "flavors" of the mind-eye experience as you progress through the illusions in this book. Among the unique visual attributes of impossible objects is their ability to perpetually defy integration. By the same token, they perpetually defy segregation!

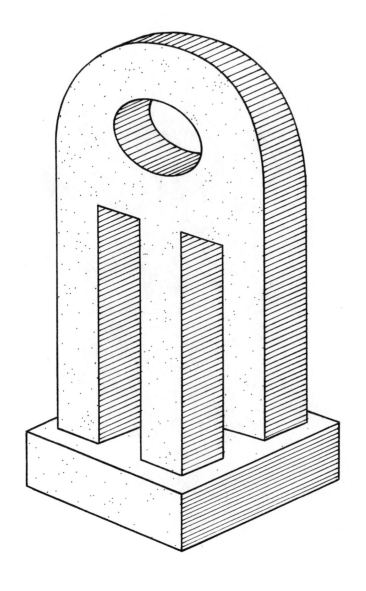

77 Where are the five people admiring these flowers?

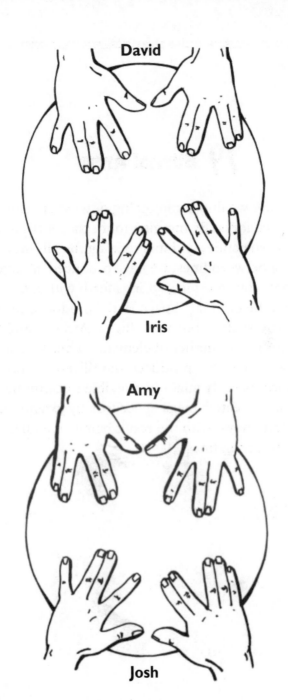

78 Of these four players, can you see which two have unusual hands?

79 Blivital Array

In this figure we find a conjoining of what appears to be several space forks. By merging four space forks into a single vertical structure, and maintaining the all-important equal spacing between lines, we have produced an object that, from only four footings, springs forth with nine tines! As you recall, the original "Space Fork" produced three tines out of two shafts—but the "Blivital Array" more than doubles the original number of elements. Thus with a little experimentation we have produced the Blivet, or Space Fork, Extraordinaire! It might be possible to continue this experiment and create a mega-space fork by extending the base works infinitely—with the result being an endless array of upward-projecting tines!

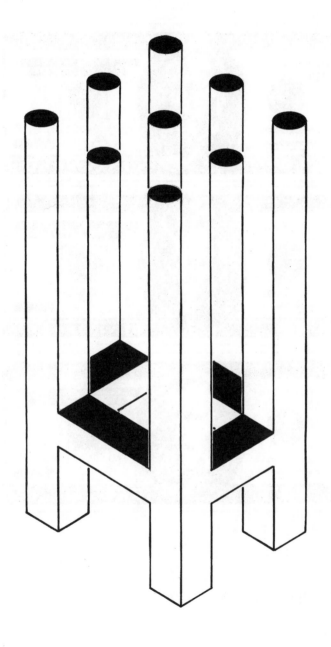

80 Which one is real?

81 Are these hoops circular?

82 Double Keys

Before we move on to the next major segment in our tour of Impossibilia we must consider a strange subset of Fork-related, stick-style entities—bars that resemble piano keys. The principle of the "Double Keys," which incorporate this effect, actually is the same as that of the "Space Fork"—false connections that cause one or more elements to retreat to a different plane. As you first glance to the left of this figure, it seems to be composed of two ends with a wide gap between them. Yet, as you look to the right you see two ends in contact, which cast a strong shadow. Once you perceive the ambiguity of the figure, your gaze seems caught up in a visual back-and-forth that may continue for some time, as you try to count the bars. It's a lot like looking at the "Space Fork," but in a fresh new way. In this case, the number of elements at each end remains the same, but one component seems to materialize out of its neighbor, while another arises out of the shadows.

Existing at the outland of reality, this figure seems to represent a prime example of both a material and nonmaterial object! In this case the shadow, which becomes part of the solid element in the foreground, reinforces the ambiguity, and an element at the right vanishes into nothingness, becoming a void at the left. It is the shadow along with false connections that creates this unique and innovative new illusion. Of course, none of this would be possible in the real world, yet here it is, the unimaginable, right before your very eyes!

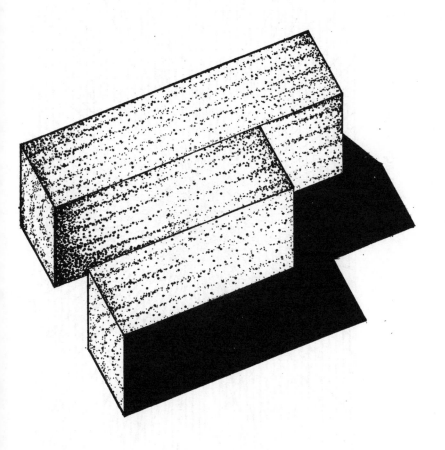

Can you see the patterns formed by the lines?

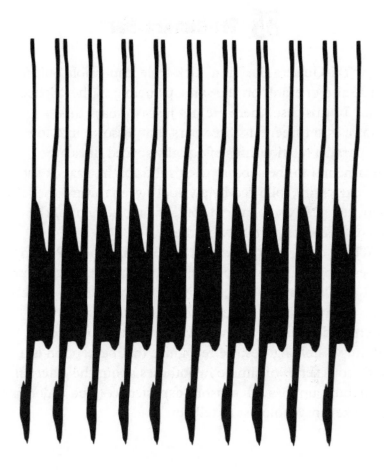

84 What are these?

85 Tri-Quadra Bar

The "Tri-Quadra Bar" is a stick-style impossible object that also operates on the same principle as the "Space Fork." In this case, there are not just two bars that dissolve into three, but three bars that dissolve into four. The parallel relationships of equally spaced lines are fundamental to the success of this illusion. A gaze at the right extremity, followed by a visual sweep toward the left, seems to cause your stare to split, as one element of the illusion becomes part of two others.

Where does reality end and impossibility begin? Many of these objects leave it up to the hardworking eye to figure that out. Our day-to-day experiences with external objects make it very difficult to accept concepts that we cannot understand intuitively. Thus, through our encounters with impossible figures, we recognize that perception is a continuous series of simple hypotheses about the external world, built up through sensory experience. (And it doesn't even take a psychologist to tell you that!)

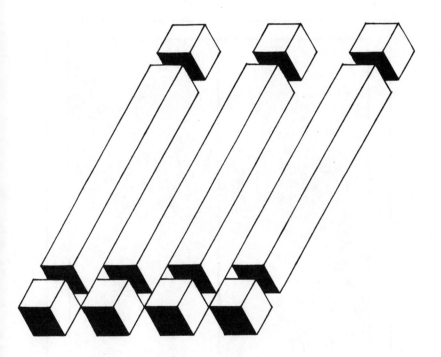

86 This is a sign on a glass door. What does it say?

87 This design has two straight lines across it. Or does it?

88 Dual-End Bi-Post

Simplicity is a virtue of profundity, for the former is what often makes for the latter. When something is clear, concise, and simple, it is often said to be brave, bold, and relevant! Now, the "Dual-End Bi-Post" may not be any of the aforementioned, because it is a contradiction, and quite impossible!

Visual communication is a universal language. It has no limits of tongue, vocabulary, or grammar, and can be perceived by the illiterate as well as the literate. Visual imagery can often convey facts and ideas in a deeper, wider, and more articulate manner than almost any other means of communication. It can reiterate and reinforce verbal concepts with such sensory richness that no one would want to add even a word! Yet (and we must drop a bomb on what has just been said) impossible objects do just the opposite: they contaminate and confuse visual communication. If we tried to verbally describe an impossible object to someone—over the telephone, for instance—the person at the other end of the line would not likely be able to draw it. Then the question might be raised: Of what use is this strange new-fangled device?

The "Dual-End Bi-Post" might, after all, have a most practical application. It could prove most valuable as a dual-purpose bi-post for shoring up a mine shaft. If the mine were to collapse, the bi-post could suddenly become two posts, thereby reinforcing the shaft and preventing the collapse in the first place!

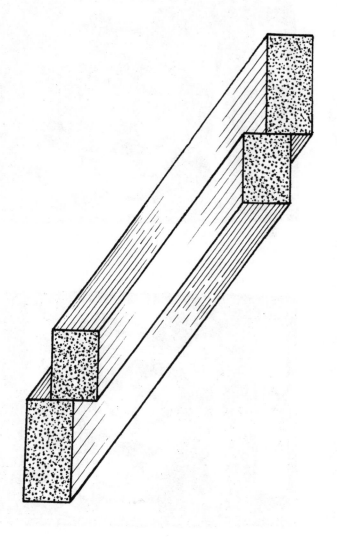

There are twelve differences between these two pictures. Can you find them all?

A

11 12 B 14 15

C

90 Is the shape at the center the letter B or
the number 13?

9 | The Crazy Crate

A new impossible object made its debut in 1966 as a result of the experiments of Dr. Charles F. Cochran, a photographer, in Chicago, Illinois. Cochran's "trick" photograph of his "Crazy Crate" appeared in the June 1966 issue of *Scientific American* magazine. Many impossiblers have since experimented with the "Crazy Crate," and now the figure stands as one of the classic "Big Four," a status shared with the "Impossible Triangle," the "Endless Staircase," and the "Space Fork." Its originator first called it the "Freemish Crate," and claimed it was "built for the shipment of optical illusions in quantity." Others have added that this impossible box is just great for carrying widgets and other unidentifiable objects.

The impossible crate is an ambiguous inside-out skeletal cube that causes a visual-mental shock when you see it, a result of the fluctuation between two opposing perceptual interpretations. A coherent solution never emerges. As in so many impossible objects, the "Crazy Crate" works through false connections in the drawing.

The immediate predecessor of the "Crazy Crate" was the "impossible box" held by a seated lad in M.C. Escher's famous 1958 etching, "Belvedere." Escher's impossible box, in turn, had its origins in the Necker Cube, which is not an impossible object but an ambiguous figure involving depth reversal.

The Necker Cube was first described in 1832 by the Swiss crystallographer Louis A. Necker, who noticed that crystals sometimes appeared to change in shape as he looked at them. The Necker Cube can be seen as a two-dimensional flat surface, but due to the way we look at things, it is actually more difficult for us to see it in two dimensions than in three. When we stare at the Necker Cube, we experience a figure alternating in depth—sometimes one face lies in the front, then the same face lies in the back. It jumps suddenly from one position to the other. Our perception goes on a dynamic search for the best interpretation of the available data. How much our past experience and learning affect our interpretation is a mystery. This factor is significant, though, in the creation of impossible objects that, like the Necker Cube, "jam" our perceptive processes.

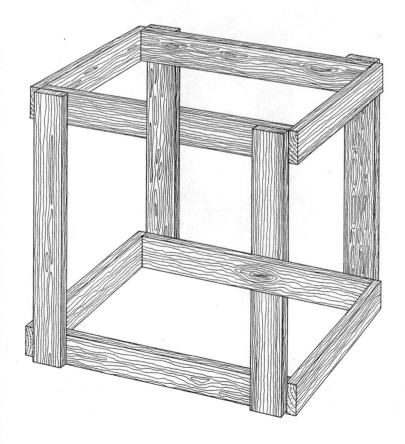

92 This monkey likes hanging around. Can you find his owner?

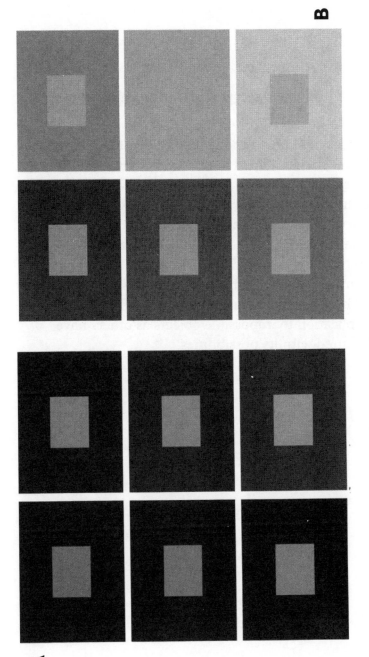

93 Is the tone in the center area of the first block A the same as the tone in the center of the last block B?

94 Necker Cube Variations

The sequence of illustrations that follow shows how the skeletal cube developed in relation to impossible objects. The image on the top shows the original Necker Cube. (Notice how the little black ball sometimes appears in the cube's front face, and sometimes in the back face, and in the corner, or center). The image to the right shows how Escher applied Necker's Cube. The image below, in turn, shows Dr. Cochran's rendition of Escher's Impossible Cube. There have been many variations of the cube in its application to impossible objects as others have experimented with its possibilities.

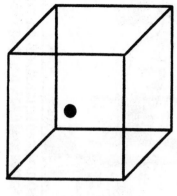

Necker's Cube

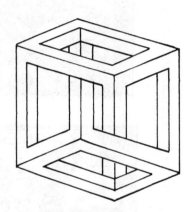

Escher's Cube

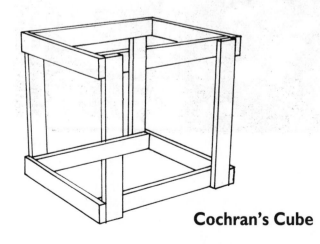

Cochran's Cube

These two pictures are not identical. Can you find the ten differences?

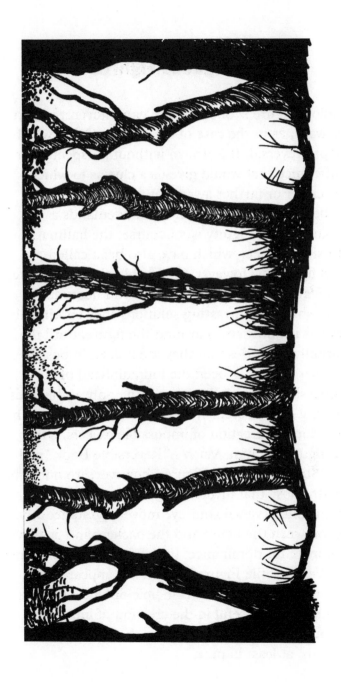

96 Can you find two sisters in the woods?

97 Ambiguous Figures

An ambiguous figure is one that you can interpret in two or more ways, as in the case of the Necker Cube, which exhibits depth reversal. It is drawn without perspective or any size difference that would give us a clue as to which part of it is closer or farther away. Yet we still see in the Necker Cube a three dimensionality that demands a concrete solution. Ambiguity is, of course, the hallmark of all impossible objects, which have also been called "ambiguous figures." However, impossible objects go a step beyond mere ambiguity. Through their wild fluctuations between two sharply contrasting solutions they continually defy the eye as it vainly roves around the figure, until the mind eventually concedes that they are indeed impossible.

The Necker Cube has been the fountainhead of all cubular impossible objects. Yet it is not the only ambiguous figure involving depth reversal, and not the only one that has been involved in the creation of impossible objects. Other ambiguous figures include Mach's "Reversible Book" and Schröder's "Staircase." These figures, however, are not to be confused with those that involve a figure-ground reversal. In a figure-ground reversal your eye moves spontaneously, alternating between the figure and the background as they seem to compete for dominance. Probably the best example is Rubin's "Vase-Profile Figure," which has appeared in print in countless versions. The principle of figure-ground reversal has also been useful in the creation of impossible objects. "Double Keys," with its strong shadows, is an example of this, at least in part.

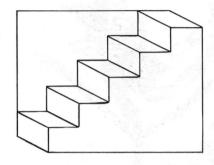

Schröder's Staircase

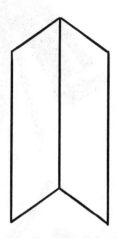

Mach's Reversible Book

Rubin's Vase-Profile

Which clowns have the longer ropes?

99 Which clowns have the longer ropes now?

100 Integral Cube

As stated earlier, the "Crazy Crate" developed from the impossible cube held by the youth in M.C. Escher's "Belvedere," which in turn was inspired by L.A. Necker's Cube. As before, one man builds upon the work of another—one man discovers or invents, a second man improvises, and a third man develops and improves! In like fashion, we now have a fourth-generation impossible cube, the "Integral Cube"—just one result of many more recent experiments with cubes. The cube is an amazingly flexible figure, capable of producing a wide range of variations. It can be modified a great deal without losing its overall identity as a cube. The example shown here, as in so many cases, functions through a depth ambiguity based on false connections.

The "Integral Cube" makes use of strange corner connections, connections that are not created in the manner we would normally expect. Front corners are not always connected to other front corners, but to side points and rear extremities. For instance, one vertical part is connected at its top end to a horizontal part that seems at first to be the top front of the cube, but then appears to be the bottom of the back side of the cube. In addition to peculiar corner connections, this figure incorporates odd shadings and other unexpected coverings and joinings.

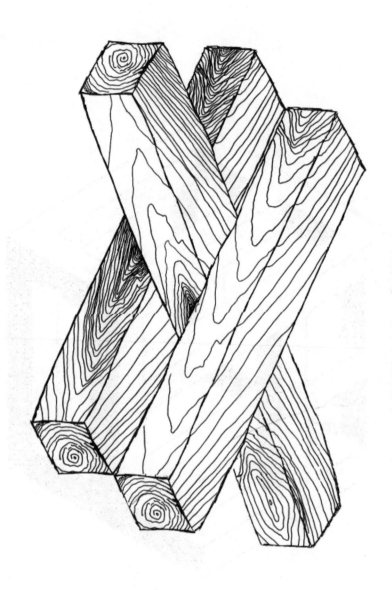

101 Where would you drill a hole to fix these three pieces of wood together?

102 Does this look flat?

103 Escalating Cube

While ambiguous depth-reversal figures throw the mind into a state of indecision, impossible cubes take us a step further into befuddlement. The concept of the impossible cube has now been telescoped into the intriguing figure dubbed the "Escalating Cube," which has expanding or reducing possibilities.

In this figure downsized cubes are developed into one entity. A thin wall on the left and a massive wall on the right share a common plane at the left and bottom, but not at the right and top. Tucked between them are ever-smaller cubes that demonstrate the same properties. The process of using still smaller cubes, or larger for that matter, could go on forever. Another name for this object, therefore, could be the "Infinity Cube."

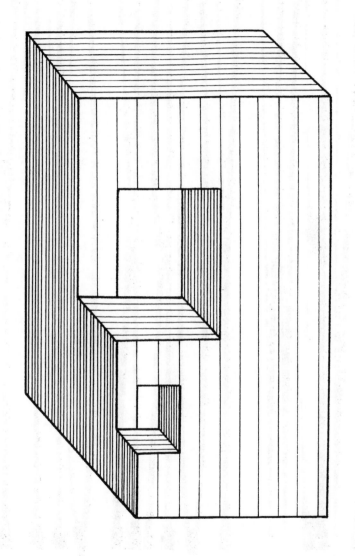

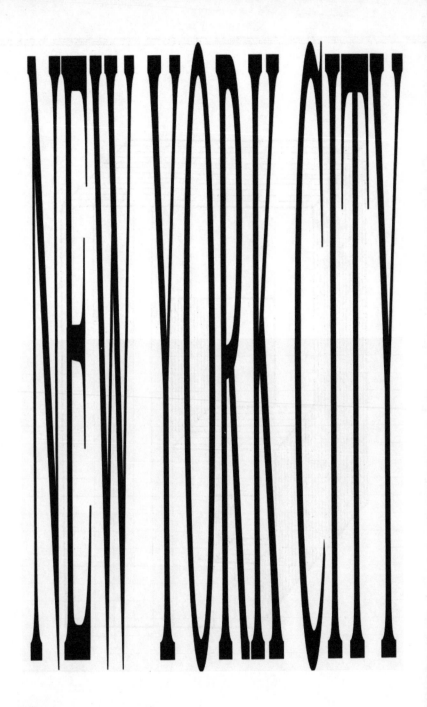

104 Where is this?

105 The table mat for your glass smiles when your glass is full. What will it do when it's empty?

106 Integral Cubicle

The "Integral Cubicle" shown on the facing page is another variation on the cube theme. At first glance, you seem to see two distinct clusters of cubes as if they were fused together. Then, on second glance, a curious discontinuity becomes evident. The right-side face of one set of cubes suddenly becomes the left-side face of the other set of cubes. As with Necker's Cube, your mind cannot decide which concept to adopt.

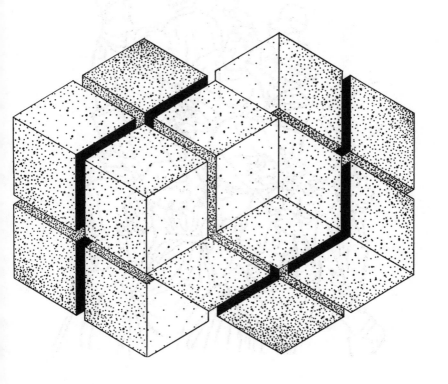

107 Everyone at the wedding is looking for Grandpa. Can you find him?

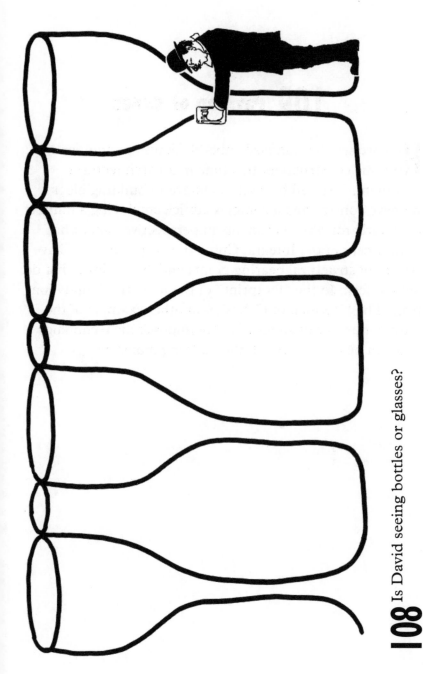

108 Is David seeing bottles or glasses?

147

109 Pavilion of Cubes

Here we see the standard cube-block unit in another unique construction, this time in an architectural treatment. Inspired by a set of children's building blocks, we have constructed a complex edifice employing a number of cleverly misplaced elements in perspective, somewhat reminiscent of the Integral Cube. In this instance we have a system of structural bearing points and "roof" lines that do not conform to the "footprint" of the floor and foundation plan. The "Pavilion of Cubes" is another example of the infinite number of applications of impossibilic technology that can be encouraged in the building industry!

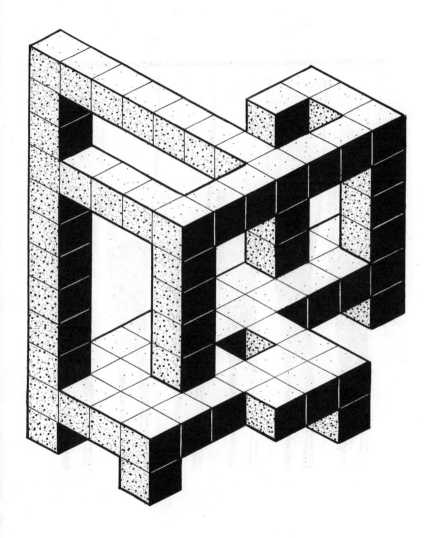

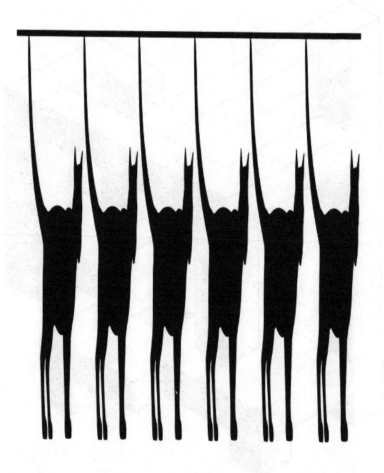

110 What is this?

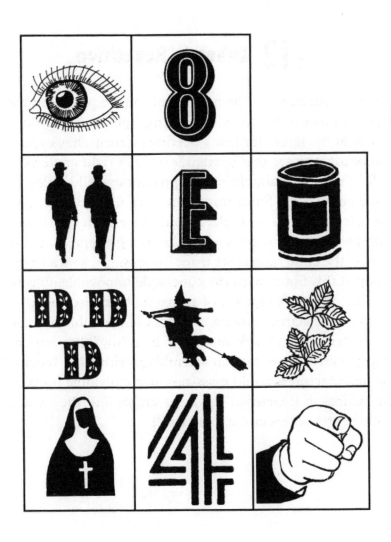

III Can you read this message?

112 Cubes in Repetition

In the illustration on the next page, you are presented with a figure that seems to exist in a single plane. After you glance at the figure for just a fleeting moment, however, you become aware that it extends out at a right angle as well, while still maintaining its apparent overall single-plane orientation. Since this figure partially incorporates the principle of the triangle, it could have been classified with the tribar. However, while the triangle represents three angles, the cube represents three dimensions, so we have grouped this figure with the cube-style impossible objects.

The children's pastime of arranging blocks seems to be a favorite activity among creators of impossible objects. In this array, each block appears to be a "toy" that can be played with and put into an assemblage with other blocks. If toy manufacturers could mass-produce individual units of the "Cubes in Repetition" on an assembly line, they would likely be top sellers at the retail level!

113 Is the dot in the center of the circle?

114 Which pen is longer—top or bottom?

115 Cubular Snowflake

In this figure we again see an impossible object that functions like the "Crazy Crate" or Escher's Impossible Box. Unlike many of the impossible figures that work on false connections and oscillating planes in perspective, the Cubular Snowflake holds together by means of a false orientation. The core element suddenly becomes tied to the outer arrangement. As in the Necker Cube, this figure seems to oscillate between concave and convex configurations.

In another sense, you could consider this figure an illustration of depth reversal, as borrowed from the Necker Cube. As we see in this example and others like it, this principle can be put to great effect in the creation of impossible worlds.

Can you spot the seven differences between these two pictures?

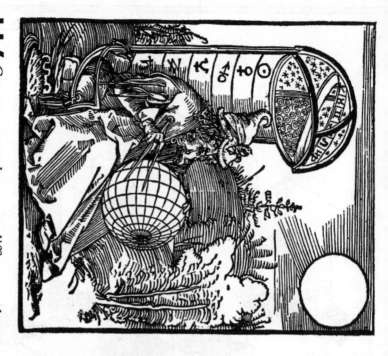

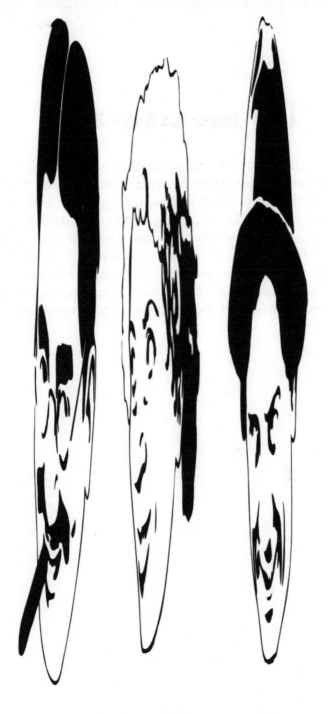

117 Who are these funny people?

118 Indented Sand Blocks

This figure functions primarily on depth-projection ambiguity. One element seems obviously in front of the other, but when you consider another portion of the element, it appears to be behind its companion piece. Meanwhile, its counterpart demonstrates the same effect. That's why we have classified it with the cube—it has one or more portions "tucked under." At the same time, at work in the figure are false connections in perspective. You might say that this figure functions on three levels. It is another impossible variation made possible by the principles of the "Crazy Crate."

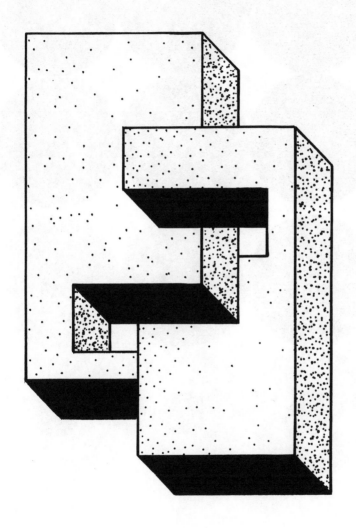

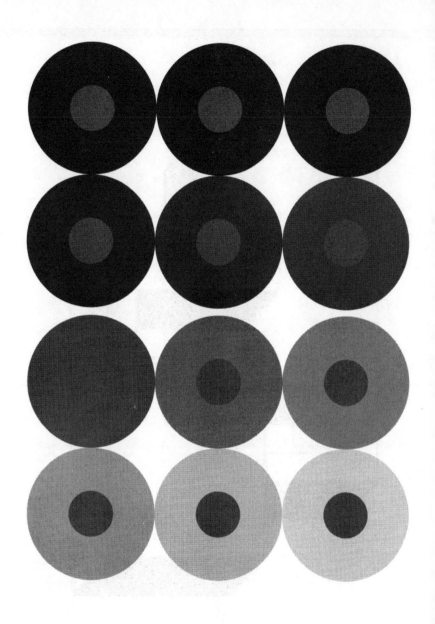

119 Which two figures have inner circles that are the same shade of grey?

120 Which O is the same height as the E next to it?

|2| **Cubes in Limbo**

The figure on the next page seems to be, at first glance, an acceptable arrangement of cubes. But, after a closer look you realize that there is something decidedly wrong. If you count the cubes they add up to four, yet the cube at the lower right is both a rear cube and a front cube at the same time. Check it out.

122 Is this a place or a person?

123 Are there any fakes?

124 Two-Story Cube

The object featured on the next page is another innovative variation of the basic impossible cube. In this figure we see what appears to be, at first glance, a structure consisting of four vertical members with cross members at mid-height. But it does not take long to see that there is something very unusual about this object. The cross members at mid-height are connected to the structure in an impossible way. They extend from the left and right verticals back to a rear vertical, which is, in reality, the front vertical—if you look at the top and bottom. In this figure we encounter a circumstance similar to that found in the "Space Fork"— confusion about the status of the middle member. If it is either the front or rear vertical, then where is the fourth vertical support? According to our view through the window at the top, there is no rear vertical. Yet, what we see at mid-height tells us that there has to be a rear vertical. The odd horizontals of this "two-story" cube seem to turn it wrong-side out—without bending it or deforming it—not even one inch!

125 Which of these pencil scribbles is longer?

Two cryptic messages:

This is the best way to get a job done. What does it say?

This is another way to describe where something originates from! What is the word?

127 Multifaceted Cinder Block

This strange new figure is yet another startling variation on the impossible cube. This time we see what at first seems a decorative concrete block for building construction or landscaping. As we look closer, however, our attention is caught by the details in its center cavity, which are oriented in an impossible manner.

We are looking at an example of planar discontinuity. This occurs where an element in the drawing appears in more than one pictorial plane. For example, the middle left-right element in the cavity exists in at least three different planes—in the face of the block, in the plane of the single top-to-bottom element in the cavity under which it dips, and then in its own position beneath the cross bars. Meanwhile, the top-to-bottom element in the cavity passes effortlessly from top to bottom, alternately dipping and rising as it weaves between the horizontals, yet it is not bent at all and shows no sign of trauma.

The two primary indicators of what's wrong in this drawing are the outside of the front, which continually tells us that the face is flat, and the center vertical element, which blatantly passes behind, and then in front, of its companions. From an architectural standpoint, a schematic like this could serve as a plan for a four-story apartment house without any need for a stairway or an elevator! This figure may also remind you of a type of construction project—a tunnel, for instance—where teams of workers start at opposite ends and dig toward a meeting point at the center, where they inevitably miss each other. Except, in this case, they don't miss!

129 Can you spot nineteen differences between these two pictures?

130 Logs and Beams

Here we open up a whole new realm of hybrid impossibilities. Up to this point the draftsman's board, straightedge, and triangle have been used to create figures.

In this unique new figure, "Logs and Beams," three beams seem to quite normally touch each other along their common edges. But, at their right angle a startling new phenomenon occurs: three massive cylinders, almost as if forced through, easily "squeeze" their way between the beams. Yet, the three beams have no space between them. How can this be? Is this a dream come true, in principle, for a new building technology that allows a person to enter a building through a closed door and go out through a wall? Perhaps it could offer an easy way to stack logs between railroad ties in a storage yard!

This figure works in a manner similar to the "Space Fork," in that it makes use of equally spaced parallel lines. The logs are simply drawn into the rails, without regard to any rule of perspective. In fact, anything you wanted could be drawn between the rails.

If this thing(s) were just a stack of firewood waiting to be ignited by a match, you might wonder about which direction the flames would burn, especially around the area of the supposed space between the beams. Indeed, "Logs and Beams" has some amazing impossibilities!

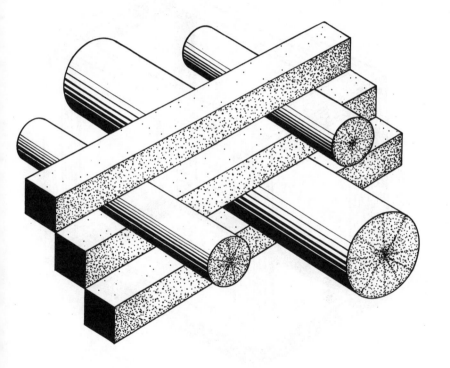

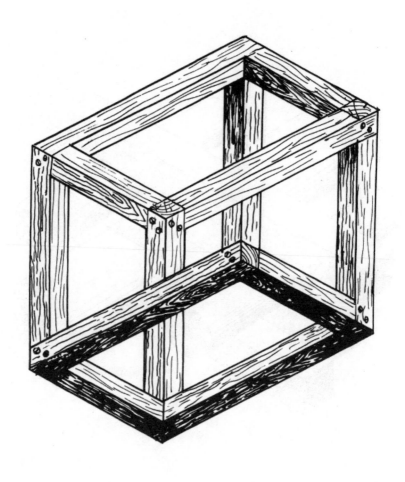

131 Could you make a box like this?

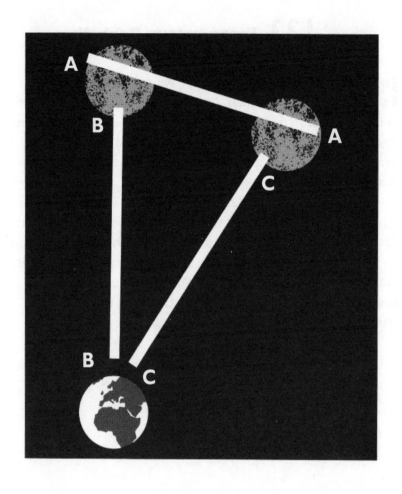

132 Which line is longer than the other two? A-A, B-B, or C-C?

133 Incongruous Barbell

In another circular impossibility we might ask: How can a straight bar wrap itself around another object without bending? The "Incongruous Barbell" is a device that seems to do just that. As you can see, the left disk or weight is drawn in a way that gives the illusion of a traversing rod that is neither bent or straight.

The "Incongruous Barbell" leaves you wondering what effect this device would have, as an exercise piece, upon the development of your biceps and triceps. The next time you go to the gym to use this piece of equipment in a workout, make sure the safety collars on your weights are secured and, by all means, check the orientation of the disks. Otherwise, it may be impossible to grip the object!

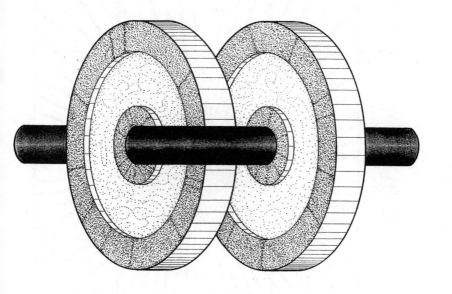

134 Stare at the black hole and the lines bend. Or are they already bent?

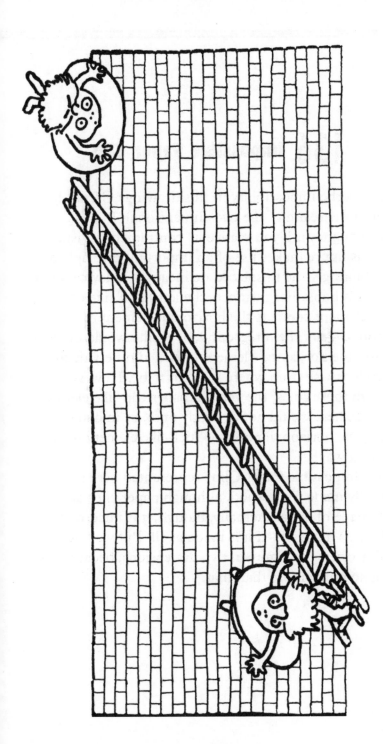

135 Beard-face Bob climbed down the ladder. "Come on down," he called.

His granddaughter Chloe was afraid she would fall. What happened?

136 Impossible Paper Clip

Where is the impossibility in this drawing? Certainly not in the realm of the two-dimensional. It looks simple enough, until you realize its contradictory visual cues. This figure makes use of an important principle of impossibiliting—the misplaced delineation, a device often used in this book. For instance, the left-hand side of the vertical element contacts the horizontal element in the background—not the foreground, as reality would demand. Likewise, the horizontal element is turned ninety degrees counterclockwise from where it ought to be. However, if we stuck with these rules, the vertical paper clip-like element that we see here would not fit neatly onto, or into and through, the horizontal popsicle-stick-like element in such a fascinating way!

The "Impossible Paper Clip" represented here is supposedly made from wood, although paper clips are usually made of metal. Actually, though, it is uncertain what this object is made of—if it is made at all! But we find it difficult to view this figure in two dimensions, because our world is so much more than that.

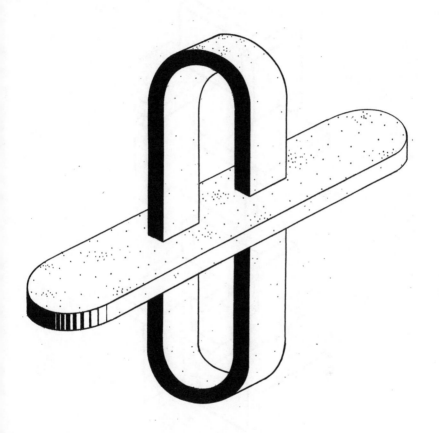

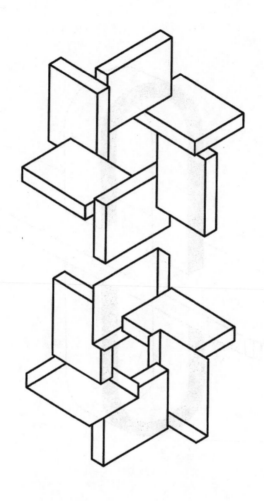

137 How are these boxes arranged?

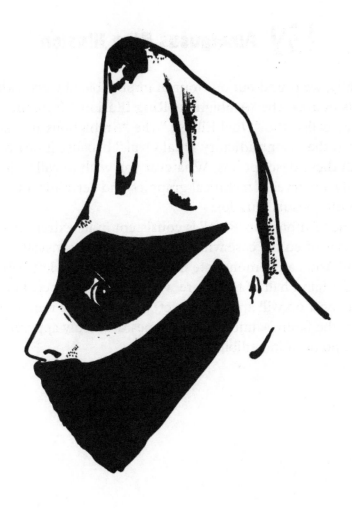

138 The robber has a dog. Can you find it?

139 Ambiguous Ring Illusion

Finally, we round out our tour of impossible objects with this figure—the "Ambiguous Ring Illusion." It might also be called the "Dual Ellipse," the "Ambiguous Ellipse," or even the "Contradictory Dual Oval," because it neatly fits all these descriptions. Whatever you wish to call it, it is truly a marvel of technical graphics and certainly a very intriguing visual paradox.

The "Ambiguous Ring" is consistent in its extremities but, as is often the case with these figures, nonsensical overall. You can demonstrate this by covering the left-hand or right-hand half of the figure with a sheet of paper. The visible portion will appear correct, but when you remove the paper, the figure's ambiguity becomes decidedly apparent, to the point of incredibility!

There are eight differences between these two pictures. Can you see them?

141 Look for a while at this page. Do the centers of the shapes seem to have a gray fuzz around them?

142 You Can Make an Impossible Object

An impossible object is actually not difficult to create. With some study of common geometric shapes, coupled with a bit of imagination, you can do it in minutes. The profound arrangement of cubes shown on the facing page was created in less than five minutes after staring at the checkerboard pattern of squares in a linoleum tile floor. After a preliminary sketch of the tile floor pattern was made, a dimension of depth was added. Then after a bit of "playing" with the figure, this unique configuration was born. Because the method of creating impossible objects follows rather narrow graphic constraints, it should come as no surprise that two people working independently might come up with a common or similar product.

The inspiration for a drawing of an impossible object may come from any one of a number of sources. The figures in this book were inspired by common everyday household items, and a few other more or less domestic items. Then, with a touch of imagination, they were reinterpreted, translated, and developed into their fullest expression. Finding potential impossible objects as such can be as exciting as a treasure hunt. It is a challenge to see how many you can find or come up with in simple sketches. Then you can give them your own names, which is even more fun!

Perhaps the best way to get started is to take sketch pad and pencil in hand and begin by sketching copies of familiar everyday objects. Don't take on anything too complicated;

stick with objects of simple geometric form. Once you've sketched something, start playing around with your idea, experimenting with it in successive drawings. It might take a little practice, but you'll be amazed at what you end up with. Your assignment, should you choose to accept it, is to create your own homemade impossible object!

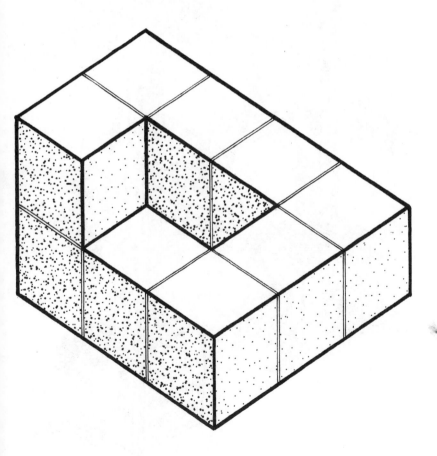

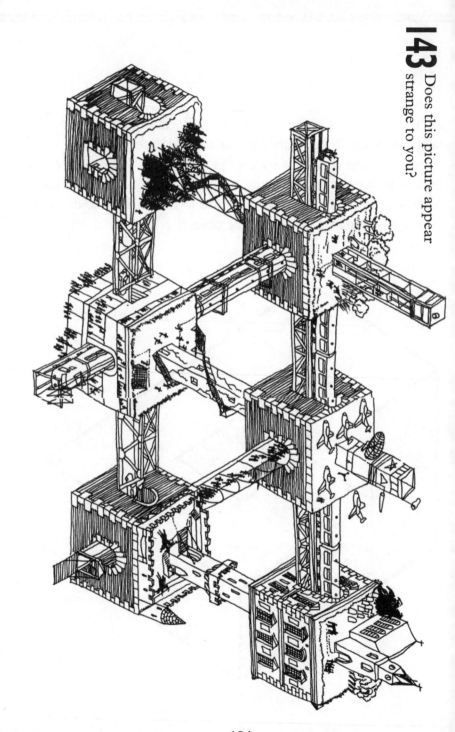

194

144 Which wallpaper pattern has stripes with the same width all the way along?

145 Space Frame

This figure was inspired by a doorway. Is it real, unreal, maybe surreal? Is it a door leading to the infinite, or a schematic design for a new kind of box frame for a bed? If the latter, perhaps such an outlandish bed might be useful in reducing sleeplessness!

In the "Space Frame" the visual ambiguity is similar to that used in many other figures in this book—false connections in perspective. If you look at one end of the figure, the bottom end for instance, you will realize that you are seeing it from a point above rather than below it, which is not consistent with the perspective of the top. In other words, we have a bird's-eye view and a worm's-eye view of the figure at the same time, which in reality is impossible. This effect has been accomplished simply by making both ends of the figure identical. This was easy enough because the three parallel lines of the long axis elements were equally spaced, making it easy to create the false connections at the ends. The unreal "Space Frame," and an inset showing how the true perspective should actually look in reality, appear on the next page.

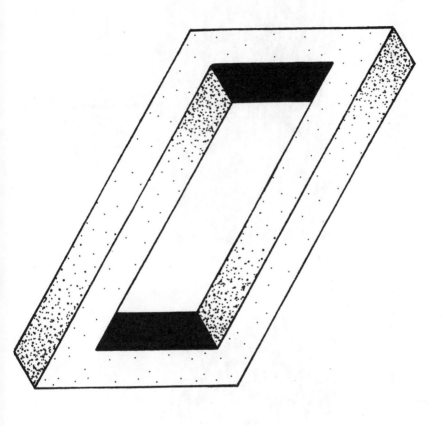

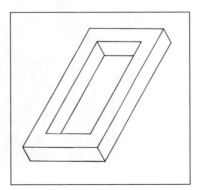

197

146 Two friends go sailing and one falls overboard. Can you find him?

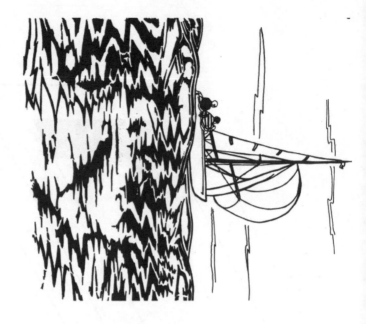

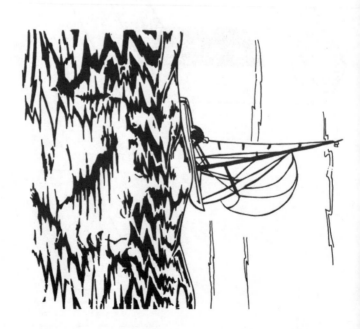

147 Can you spot the twenty differences between these two pictures?

148 Double Space Frame

To create this drawing we simply took the doorway theme of the last figure one step further. This illusion has three parallel vertical elements, all apparently on the same plane, and a top and bottom that appear to cross each other perpendicularly and in duplicate. What appears at the top is not so at the bottom, and what appears at the bottom is not so at the top. Using misplaced connections in perspective by taking advantage of equally spaced parallel lines, as before we get both a bird's-eye and a worm's-eye view at the same time. The "Double Space Frame" consists of the elements of a perfectly normal frame as seen from two different directions and, as a whole, it seems to be an intact spatial structure.

While this object may seem to resemble a warped double window frame, the similarity is only apparent. You can be sure that officials at the building trades commission would be at a loss to find an entry for it in their product listings! Then again, and just perhaps, it may be that alleged window to infinity. Could there be such a thing in the physical universe?

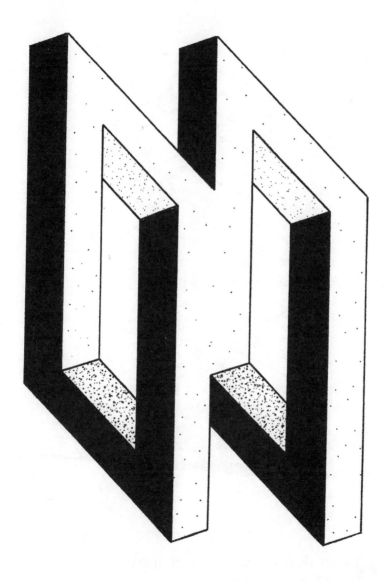

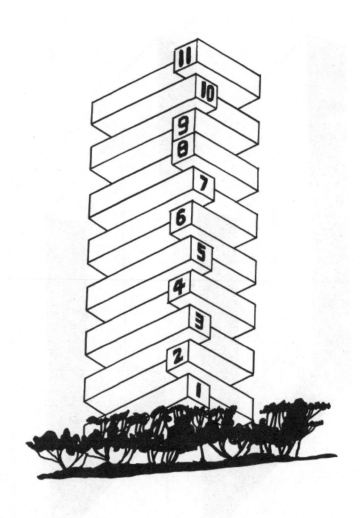

149 How does this eleven-story apartment block only have eight balconies?

150 Can you help this man to find the burglar hiding in his house?

|5| Double Clevis

Here is another unique innovation direct from the world of the impossible, the anomalous "Double Clevis." One of many figures developed from the tribar, it seems, at first glance, to exist in a single geometric plane, but then you realize that it exists in two planes at right angles to each other. Still, overall, you feel it is a one-plane figure.

You can create your own "Double Clevis," or any other double-whatever, by cleaving to the principles mentioned in this book and taking a good look at the myriad of inspirations that surround you in your everyday life. Then, just use your imagination. Oh, yes, don't forget to think of a sensible, or nonsensical, name for your invention!

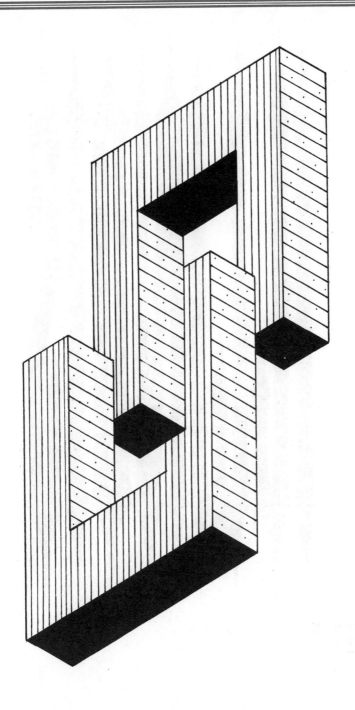

152 Which U.S. state is this?

153 Susan says she's drawn an ancient Egyptian.

Pamela says she's drawn their dad yelling at them. Who is right?

207

154 Notched Brick

The "Notched Brick" resembles a cube of butter or fudge with a bionic bite taken out of it. The vertical surface at the foreground appears as a single flat plane in perspective, yet when you look at the elements on either side of the cleavage more carefully, they seem to oscillate uncontrollably between two separate planes. The element to the left of the slot seems to hover in a position farther back than the right element. Meanwhile, the top surface seems to show the same eerie behavior, also occupying two planes in perspective. As with many other impossible objects, the convincingly confusing effect of this object is accomplished by means of misplaced connections.

The "Notched Brick," inspired by a scrap of lumber at a construction site (or it could have been a brick) is a rectangular solid—one of the easiest geometric forms to work with in creating impossible objects. To examine and "play" with different ways in which you can "redesign" such a geometric solid, start by just drawing lines!

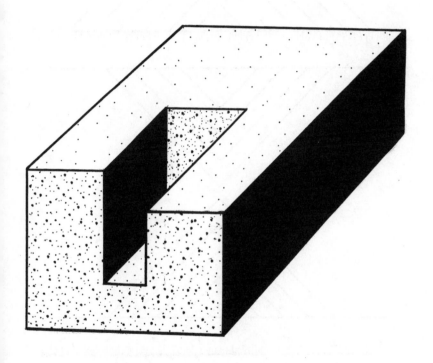

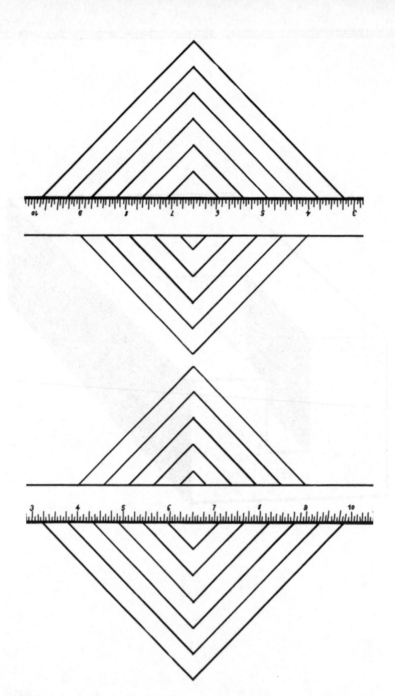

155 How many squares are there under the rulers?

156 Which line finishes at B—is it A1 or A2?

|57 Replicating Cube

Impossible cubes know no limit. Each new variety goes a step further than the last, throwing the mind into a further state of confused delight. Like its simpler predecessor, the "Escalating Cube," the "Replicating Cube" has a row of expanding or reducing windows. In this figure, which resembles the starting gate at a race track, upsized cubes are developed into more expanded entities, which could conceivably be expanded forever.

In another sense, the "Replicating Cube" could be the inspiration for a unique architectural innovation. The sills of the four windows seem to be aligned in a straight row, but then, as you look at the top of the figure, it seems obvious that they are not. You could argue with yourself, "Yes, they are," "No, they're not," "Yes, they are," ad infinitum, and you'd both be right! As with the "Escalating Cube," this figure poses no limit to the ardent and imaginative cuboholic!

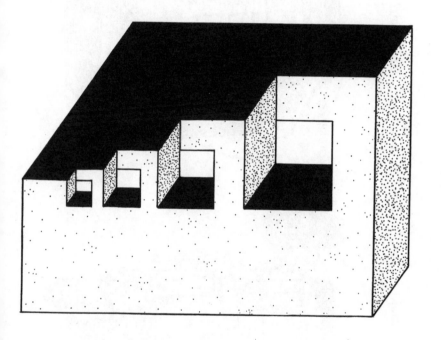

158 Can you spot the twenty differences between these two pictures?

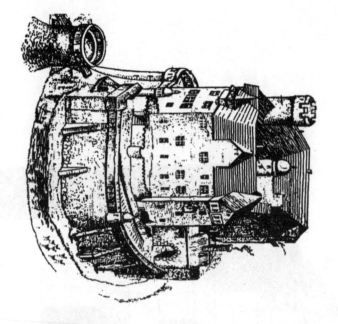

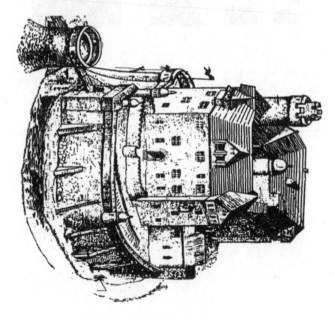

214

159 What do you see when you stare at this?

160 Opposing Timbers

The figure shown on the facing page uses the same bird's-eye/worm's-eye line connection technique as the "Dual-End Bi-Post." As before, two opposing ends of the same entity project into the foreground, but in a unique new design. As before, even though in real life this figure would have to be bent 180 degrees in order to accomplish what we see, there appears to be no evidence of trauma or torsion in the material, no cracks, ripples, or any other production flaws!

What scientists, politicians, or journalists would not love to get their hands on one of these?! It would be a great toy for fidgeting with during lengthy strategy meetings or press conferences. Or, could it be used as a fantastic futuristic interdimensional combination stun gun and communications device for space travelers? The "Opposing Timbers" may indeed be one of those upcoming by-products of impossible research where funding is poured into a financial black hole. Wouldn't these little jewels sell like hotcakes at the next Trek convention? Why not begin now to invent your very own version of the "Opposing Timbers"? You might just really stun someone!

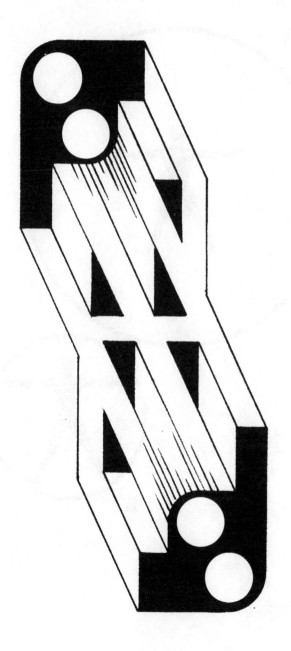

A

B

161 Which man is larger—A or B?

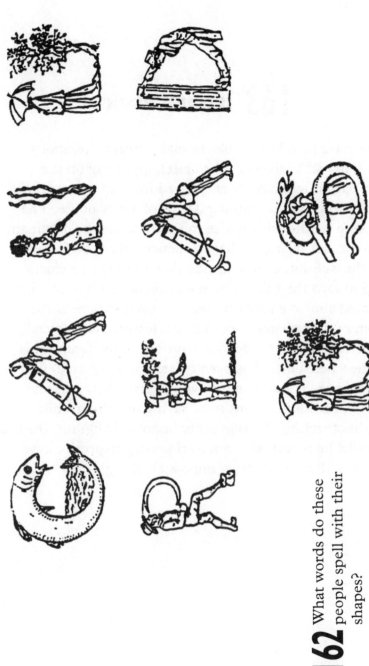

What words do these people spell with their shapes?

219

163 Integral Block

As we have seen before, blocks make great inspirations for impossible objects. The object appearing on the facing page might have been derived from an arrangement of wood studs in the framing details of a new house. The first thing we probably notice in this figure is the dominant clean-cut, left-facing U-shaped element, then, an instant later, the well-integrated, upside-down reverse-J element facing toward the right. The sensation of depth in the figure is created almost entirely by the darkened surface at the bottom of the apparent slot. Yet this feature contradicts the correspondingly shaded top surface of the figure. It is as if the whole object has been twisted, or contorted, in order to make it stand on its own integrity. Yet, it has no integrity, because it seems to be saying one thing while doing another! Again, as in other impossible figures, the use of parallel lines and false connections in perspective have joined together in this truly impossible thing!

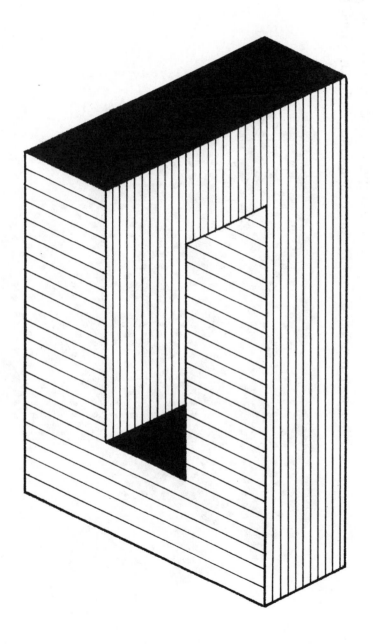

164 Sam is trying to count how many dice there are. Can you help?
Now turn this page upside down.
Joseph is counting the dice from this side. How many are there?

222

165 Why are Tom and Lenny having trouble building their barn?

166 Self-Embracing Block

In a mixture of cubular and tribar elements, this object exists by virtue of a "twist" in perspective, in a similar technique to the one used in the "Space Frame," "Double Space Frame," and the "Opposing Timbers." In this case, it is as if your eyes have been widened so that they are farther apart in order to see around both sides of the figure. Of course, through a trick of perspective, this amazing new power lies in the figure itself, not in you. It seems that the only power you feel, as you mentally embrace this figure, is the power to be confused! If you are interested in contesting that theory, try building a model!

167 When Peter goes fast does the mark on his tire travel in a circle?

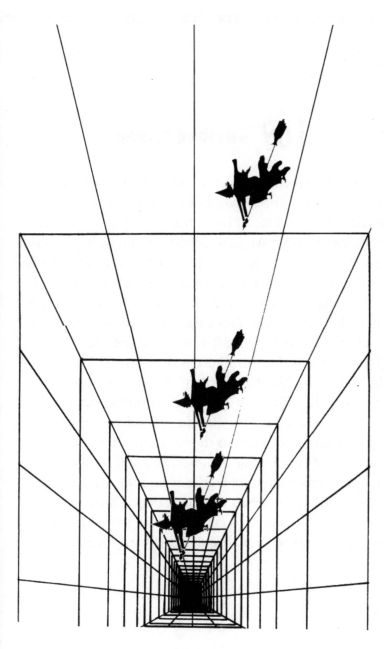

168 Does the witch get bigger and bigger as she enters the time tunnel?

227

169 Stubbed Tribar

This figure represents a clear message on how easy it is to be innovative in the world of the impossible. The "Stubbed Tribar" seems to be a cross between a cube and a tribar. However, what we have accomplished here is a simple "cut and repair" at the top corner, which results in a whole new image. The dominant left vertical shaft leads upward to the newly created level plane at the top. When you cross it, you are led, in a roundabout way, back "down" to the bottom at the base of the shaft where you started.

The inspiration for this figure is the "Impossible Triangle," but the "Stubbed Tribar" was not developed directly from the tribar but by using the same principle used to create the tribar. By playing around with the tribar concept, kicking it around, so to speak, and trying out various ways of connecting the lines, you will undoubtedly end up with something that works as an impossible object (you will know when that happens). Through such experiments it is possible to come up with many unique and innovative new objects that are decidedly impossible!

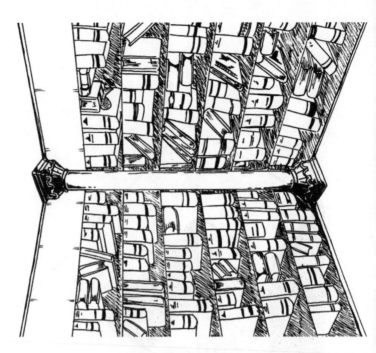

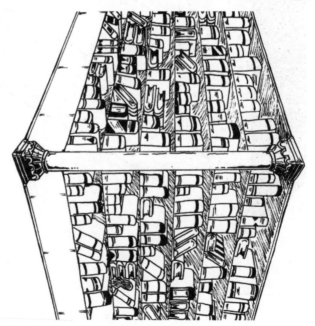

171 These hunters are searching for animals in the forest. How many can you find?

231

172 Celestial Quadra-Bar

Finally, we conclude this tour of Impossibilia with the "Celestial Quadra-Bar." This device is composed of single-entity elements, and you cannot tell for sure if they are joined or unjoined. Here, as in the "Space Fork," we experience a vibrant visual oscillation induced by the indecipherability of the figure. Even though impossible figures like this may be made up of the simplest of elements, they still retain the power to provide us with some most entertaining mental consternation.

With a single bar, which is not much to look at, you can't do much that is impossible except to reorient the ends in an impossible way, as in the "Opposing Timbers." However, this well-integrated assembly of impossible bars shows what you can accomplish by connecting two or more of these single entities. When the simple bars are joined together in a "gang bar," as we see here, the overall figure takes on a whole new dimension. You might say that these very useful single-bar components are like the side limbs that someone swiped off the infamous "Impossible Triangle" and experimented with.

At your first encounter with the "Celestial Quadra-Bar" your eye-brain system automatically accepts the bars as solid objects. Then, when you start to see that they aren't really solid, you experience a struggle, since your mind's eye cannot decide what to do with them. The figure has a strong sense of solidity about it, especially at the top and bottom, but when you scan the opposing ends of the seemingly solid bars, they simply vanish into airy nothingness!

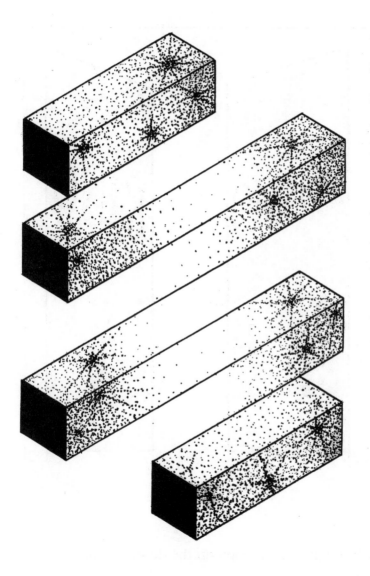

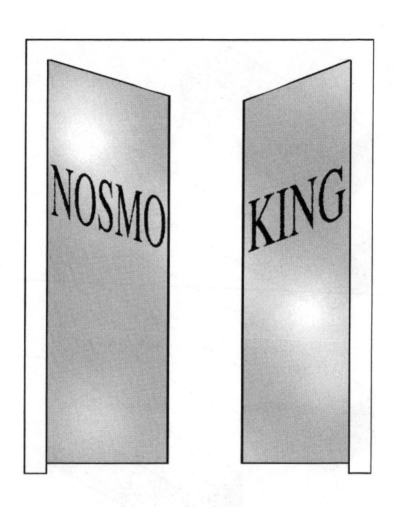

173 What does the sign on the doors mean?

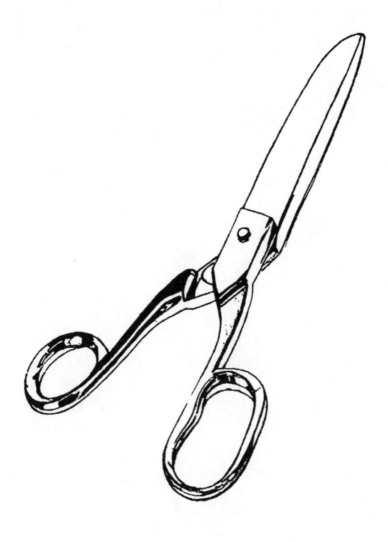

174 What is unusual about these scissors?

Answers

The following pages have explanations and pictorial answers to solve the puzzles contained within this book.

2 No—it's another visual trick.

3 The message reads: "Reader, before you judge you should open your soul to my defense."

5 There are 36 blocks in the top shape and 48 in the bottom one.

6 Neither. The spider and the butterfly are the same distance from the line.

8 It's amazing but those in A are real squares; those in B are distorted so that they look square.

9 Turn the page upside down to see a different person.

11 The lady on the right is a brunette, the lady on the left a blonde—both share the same eye.

12 They could not have built it. Every time you look at the shapes they seem connected in different ways.

14 Both pyramids are the same size.

15 The corner columns of the top floor seem to be directly above those on the lower floor, but on the top floor the front of the building is on the left of the picture and on the bottom floor the front of the building seems to be on the right.

17 Turn the page upside down and you will find seven animals. Their locations are revealed in picture answer 17.

18 All the plowed rows are parallel; they only look broader or narrower because of the marks in their sides.

20 The middle bill is a fake. The words say "Twenty Dollars" but the numbers say 25. Look at picture answer 20.

21 The regular distortion in the lines makes the surface look as if it's rolling up and down.

23 Hold the page so that the left-hand edge is at the bottom. Then turn it so that the right-hand edge is at the bottom.

24 As the black and white shapes get smaller and smaller, they seem to get less distinct and form gray areas.

26 Turn the page upside down.

27 Hold the page straight and you will see the lovers' faces in the sky and water. Look at picture answer 27.

29 Turn the page upside down and then hold the edge close to your eye. The shape does not form words; it is the alphabet.

30 Six letters: WMHEGO. I bet you forgot about the encircling O.

32 The bomber on the right-hand side is bigger.

33 Both the buckets are the same size.

35 This is a wonderful visual trick drawn by Gustave Verbeek. If you turn the page upside down, you will find his granddaughter.

36 Each state seal has a different error on the facing page. Look at picture answer 36.

38 The sign repeats the letter A: one on the second line and one on the third.

39 Simply turn the page upside down.

41 Slowly bring the pages closer and closer to your face and the center arch disappears.

42 It reads: "Choose a job that you like and you will not have to work a day in your life."

44 Another two-faced visual trick.

45 The regular pattern of black squares with narrow white spaces between them form, in your mind's eye, gray patches at the corners of the blue squares.

47 Turn the page upside down and if Frank is not clear, see picture answer 47 to find out where he is.

48 Both spoons are the same size.

50 Turn the page so that the right-hand edge is at the bottom. If you still cannot find his cat, look at picture answer 50.

51 There are ten cats. Look at picture answer 51 if you cannot find them.

53 The monkey labeled C. All the monkeys hold their left hands up to their mouths, monkey C holds his right hand up.

54 Hold the book up to your eye level and look across the page from the right-hand edge. It reads "PRESIDENT OF THE UNITED STATES."

56 You cannot have five candles filling a seven-candle holder. The illusion is caused by confusing the candles with the spaces between them.

57 Simply turn the page upside down to see the second facial expression.

59 The lines on the disks are vertical—it's the background that slopes.

60 Although it does not look it, the arches are the same on both sides. Look at picture answer 60 for the drawing without the column in the center.

62 The message reads: "MIMICRY IS THE SINCEREST FORM OF FLATTERY."

63 Hold the left-hand edge to your eye level and you will see Britain and the United States.

65 Bob. Lauren's poles are farther apart at the top.

66 The fly can be on either side of the log, depending on how you look at it. If you focus on the edge at the bottom of the picture, the fly is on the top side of the log. If you focus on the top side of the log, then the fly appears to be on the bottom of the log.

68 If you turn the page so that the left edge is at the bottom, hold it at arms length, and squint, you can see Mount Rushmore.

69 He is lying on the ground—check out picture answer 69.

71 Turn the page so that the right-hand side is at the bottom. Then you may recognize the shapes. If you don't, see picture answer 71.

72 It's not a spiral, it's a set of rings within rings.

74 Turn the page upside down to find him.

75 The center die has two sides marked five (5).

77 There are five faces. If you cannot find them look at picture answer 77.

78 Iris has two right hands and Josh has six fingers on his right hand.

80 The middle bill. The twenty-dollar bill has Jackson's face, not Grant's. Look at visual trick No. 20 or look at a twenty-dollar bill.

81 They are circles but they appear irregular.

83 Where the lines cross they form patterns which do not exist but seem to form waves.

84 Turn the page upside down and look across the surface. There are ten dogs.

86 The letters are on the other side of the door; they say "WAY OUT."

87 The lines are bent inward. If they were straight the background would make them look bent. See visual trick No. 134.

89 Did you find all twelve? Check picture answer 89.

90 Both, depending on whether you are reading across or down.

92 Turn the page upside down to find the owner.

93 Yes. The background makes them look different but they are the same.

95 How many did you find? Check your discoveries with picture answer 95.

96 The gaps between the trees form the figures. Look at picture answer 96.

98 All the ropes are the same length.

99 The clowns at the top have the longer ropes.

101 You cannot fix the pieces together. Look at the ends of the piece on the top and the piece on the bottom. The piece on top is not directly above the piece on the bottom—it just seems to be when you look at the middle of the image.

102 As the black and white shapes get smaller toward the middle, they seem to bend the surface of the page.

104 Look across the page from the edge. The shapes will read "NEW YORK CITY."

105 Turn the page upside down to see.

107 See picture answer 107 to find him.

108 David can see four glasses or three bottles.

110 Hold the lower edge close to your eyes, look across the page, and you will see six cats.

111 The message reads: "I ate too many candies which leaves none for you."

113 Yes, the stripes make the dot seem closer to the bottom, but it is in the center.

114 Both pens are the same size.

116 Did you spot all seven? See picture answer 116 to find out what they are.

117 The Marx Brothers. Hold the page close to your eyes and look across the page.

119 All the inner circles are the same shade of grey, only the outside circles change.

120 The one at the top.

122 It's Charlie Chaplin. Turn the page upside down and look across it from the edge.

123 The middle one. It should read " THE UNITED STATES _OF_ AMERICA." See picture answer 123.

125 Both scribbles are the same length.

126 The top picture says "AROUND TO IT." The bottom picture says "EMANATE."

128 Neither. The left-hand S and 8 have a narrow top and the right-hand ones a narrow bottom.

129 Were you able to find all nineteen? Check your discoveries with picture answer 129.

131 Nobody can, it's a visual trick.

132 All the lines are the same length.

134 The lines are straight.

135 Turn the page upside down to find out.

137 Their arrangement is impossible, the drawing is a visual trick.

138 Turn the page upside down.

140 Did you find eight differences? Check your discoveries with picture answer 140.

141 The closer the tiny patterns are the more they merge.

143 The blocks are not in any possible real arrangement.

144 The stripes in the top picture are all the same width. Some of the stripes in the bottom picture are wider at one edge than the other.

146 Turn the page so that the left-hand edge is at the bottom and you will find the missing sailor, or consult picture answer 146.

147 Did you spot all twenty? Check your discoveries with picture answer 147.

149 The numbers sometimes refer to balconies and sometimes to the gaps between the balconies.

150 He is near the fire. You can find him in picture answer 150.

152 Look across the page from the right-hand edge, and it will read "ILLINOIS."

153 Both. Look from the left side for Susan's and the right for Pamela's.

155 There are six. See picture answer 155.

156 Both Al and A2 finish at B.

158 Did you find twenty differences? Check picture answer 158.

159 The pattern forms stars.

161 Both men are the same size.

162 The people spell: "CAN U READ US."

164 From Sam's side 32; from Joseph's side 31.

165 What Tom and Lenny are building is impossible.

167 The mark on Peter's wheel does not go round and round. It hops forward as the wheel goes along the ground. Check it out in picture answer 167.

168 No she doesn't. She is always the same size.

170 No. Both columns are the same size.

171 There are twenty-six animals hiding. Check picture answer 171.

173 When the doors close they read "NO SMOKING."

174 When the arms of the scissors are open the blades are shut.

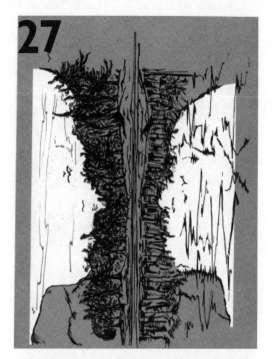

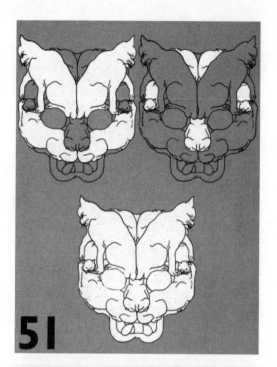

51

60

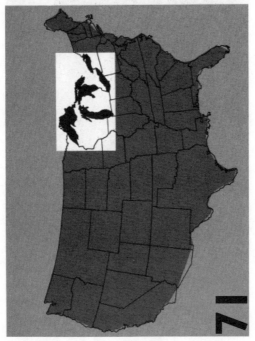

80

255

89

Wer recht bescheyden wol werden
Der pit got auff erden trumhye

95

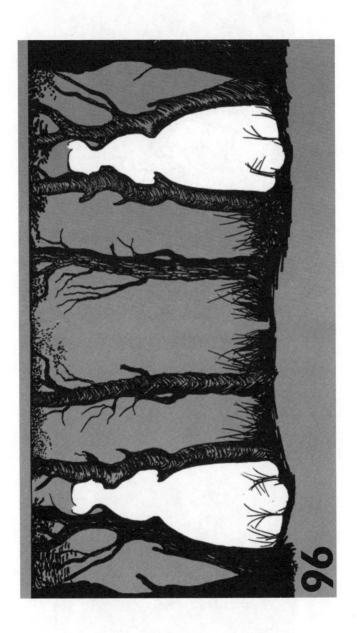

96

123

129

140

146

147

150

155

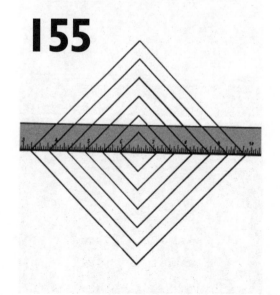

158

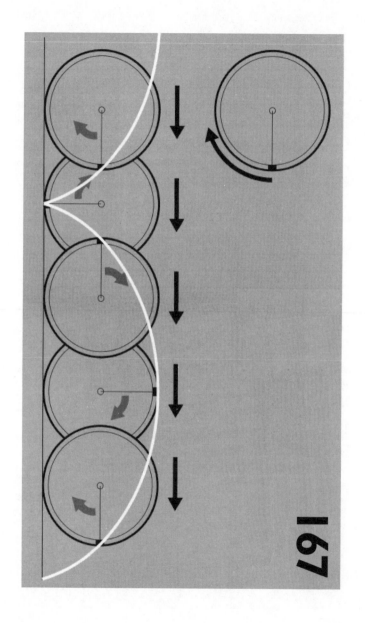

171

265

Index

All the puzzles in this book have been classified according to the methods they use to outwit you.

MISCELLANEOUS